# Dynamic Test Generator
## with Electronic Testing and Grade Book

Algebra 2

## HOLT, RINEHART AND WINSTON

A Harcourt Classroom Education Company

**Austin** • New York • Orlando • Atlanta • San Francisco • Boston • Dallas • Toronto • London

**Photo Credit**
Front Cover: Tom Paiva/FPG International.

TestCheck is a trademark of Renaissance Learning.

Printed in the United States of America

ISBN 0-03-066382-2

2 3 4 5 6 7   082   05  04  03  02  01

# Table of Contents

**Item Listing Printout**

# About the Algebra 2 Dynamic Test Generator with Electronic Testing and Grade Book

The Dynamic Test Generator with Electronic Testing and Grade Book CD-ROM can be found inside the back cover. The CD-ROM contains TestCheck™, which consists of three components—**Worksheet Builder** is a flexible test generator, **Management Module** performs all student/teacher/classroom gradebook functions, and **Student Module** allows students to take tests and review their performance on screen. Because TestCheck can be networked, teachers and administrators can share tests, worksheets, and student records on a local area network.

The **Worksheet Builder** can

- handle virtually all types of assessment items—multiple choice, free response, fill-in-the-blank, matching, true/false, and rubric-scored.
- generate different but equivalent items for each student using the patented algorithm and distractor-shuffling technology.
- create paper tests or on-screen tests, or output assessment items in an Internet-ready format.
- format assessments in many ways.
- allow teachers to add or edit questions through a powerful authoring tool.
- create Cartesian, polar, and line graphs using the function plotter tool.
- print worksheets, create separate answer sheets, and set due dates.

The **Management Module** makes grading and record keeping quick and easy, helping to track and record the history of each student and course. This module will quickly

- generate answer sheets.
- generate reports.
- establish class records.
- add students (manually or via an import function).
- set passwords.
- establish grading scales.
- view or print reports.

Reports may provide information on student history, student name, class history, class assignments, and class concept mastery.

The **Student Module** allows students to complete assignments, review them, and have them automatically scored—all on screen.

This supplement to *Algebra 2* contains

- the Algebra 2 Dynamic Test Generator with Electronic Testing and Grade Book.
- a Getting Started Guide, which includes installation instructions for the TestCheck system.
- objectives for each lesson in *Algebra 2*.
- a printed listing of all problem types that are contained in Worksheet Builder, the dynamic test generator.
- printed answers to prepared worksheets and chapter tests.

A mid-chapter test and three prepared chapter tests for each chapter can be found in electronic form on the CD-ROM.

TestCheck includes a user-friendly help system built into the program that assists you while you become familiar with the efficient use of each component. Most dialog boxes contain help buttons that access descriptive information, and you can also access the TestCheck help system from the main Help menu.

HRW has assembled a team of dedicated technical and teaching professionals and a comprehensive service program to provide you with the support you need. The following may be used to obtain technical support for any HRW software product.

Online Help: www.hrwtechsupport.com
email: tschrw@hrwtechsupport.com
HRW Technical Support Center: (800) 323-9239
7 A.M. to 10 P.M. Central Time on regular business days

# Getting Started Guide

## System Requirements

To run TestCheck on your computer it must meet the minimum system requirements listed below:

### Microsoft Windows®

- 60 MHz Pentium processor-based computer
- 16 MB of installed RAM
- 50 MB of free disk space
- Microsoft Windows 95, 98, or NT
- CD-ROM drive

### Macintosh®

- 66 MHz Power Macintosh
- 12 MB available RAM
- 50 MB of free disk space
- Mac OS 7.5.5 or later
- CD-ROM drive

## Installing TestCheck™

### Microsoft Windows®

1. Insert CD in CD-ROM drive. Once loaded, double-click on "My Computer" (on your desktop) and double-click on whichever drive shows the CD and "TestCheck."
2. Find the **Setup.exe** icon and double-click on it. This will begin the installation.
3. For the next three windows, simply accept the defaults and click [Next>] for each.
4. Once the setup is complete, * remove the disk, and restart your computer by clicking [Finish]. The TestCheck software is now loaded.

   **\*Note:** The disk includes an online user's manual called *User's Guide* which requires Adobe Acrobat® Reader. If you do not already have this program on your computer, it is provided for you on the disk. Look for the **Ar40eng.exe** icon to install that as well.

### Macintosh®

1. Insert CD in drive. When the TestCheck icon appears on the desktop, double-click to open.
2. Double-click on the TestCheck 2.0 Install icon.
3. Click [Continue] on the Welcome! screen.
4. Click [Install] to load all components.
5. Click [Install] again to load to the Hard Drive.
6. If Adobe Acrobat® Reader is not installed on your computer, click [OK] on this screen and then [Install] on the next to load it. (You'll need AR to open the online *User's Guide*.)
7. Once installation is complete, click [Quit], and finally, [Restart].

## Network Installation

When installing TestCheck on a network system, be sure the data location selected is on the network server. This will allow every workstation with TestCheck installed to access the student database. Each individual workstation must have TestCheck individually installed but pointed toward the same data location on the network. For ease of use in the future it is strongly recommended that you now record the path to, and the name of, the data location.

TestCheck has a 400-student limit for each data location. To increase student capacity you will have to create additional data locations on the server, in completely different folders.

## Registering Your Copy of TestCheck™

1. From the Start button, go to Programs, then TestCheck. Select TestCheck - Management. *Mac Users:* From either Launcher or the Hard Drive, open the TestCheck folder, and select TestCheck™ Management.

2. Follow system prompts until New Registration appears. Enter your school's name and location, and then your name in the appropriate fields. Click [Next>].

3. The next panel that appears is Data Location Choices (see below). If you wish to create a new folder for your data location, select the "Create a new location for data" option. TestCheck will automatically create a special database in this location that will allow you to share data with multiple computers. This panel also gives you the option of selecting an existing folder. This would only be applicable if your school maintained a compatible student database or owned a previous version of TestCheck. The sample data provided may be used to become familiar with the program itself.

To select a data option, click the radio button in front of your choice, then click the [Next] button.

4. When the Select Location panel appears, click the [Select Location] button.

5. In the dialog box that follows, select the specific folder you wish to use for your TestCheck data. (To create a new folder on the Macintosh, click the [New folder] button.

In Windows, click the New Folder icon 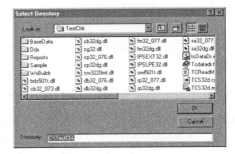. Name the folder, open it, then select it for the data location.)

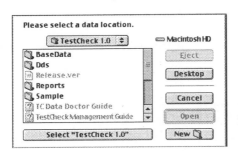

6. After selecting the appropriate location for your data, click [Select "Folder Name"] for Macintosh, or [OK] for Windows. This will return you to the Select Location panel of the Registration Assistant and display your information. Click [Next] to continue.

7. Click [Finish] or [Done] to complete the registration. The TestCheck Management module will automatically begin but requires a password.

8. The default administrator password is **admin**, but see Chapter 5 of the *User's Guide* for more information about setting user passwords. Click [OK].

9. You are now ready to begin using the software.

## The Sample Data

Previewing TestCheck through use of the Sample Data is an excellent way to introduce yourself to the application. Perhaps you chose to do this in Step 3 during Data Location Choices, but now you want to select your *permanent* location. To return to the proper panel and initiate this procedure, follow these easy steps:

• Open TestCheck Management and click [School]

• Click [Preferences] and then double-click on [Data Location] to return to the Data Location Choices screen. Make your new selection and proceed as before.

# Lesson Objectives

**Chapter 1 - Data and Linear Representations**

Lesson 1 - Tables and Graphs of Linear Equations
Objective 1 - Represent a real-world linear relationship in a table, graph, or equation.
Objective 2 - Identify linear equations and linear relationships between variables in a table.

Lesson 2 - Slopes and Intercepts
Objective 1 - Graph a linear equation.
Objective 2 - Write a linear equation for a given line in the coordinate plane.

Lesson 3 - Linear Equations in Two Variables
Objective 1 - Write a linear equation in two variables given sufficient information.
Objective 2 - Write an equation for a line that is parallel or perpendicular to a given line.

Lesson 4 - Direct Variation and Proportion
Objective 1 - Write and apply direct-variation equations.
Objective 2 - Write and solve proportions.

Lesson 5 - Scatter Plots and Least-Squares Lines
Objective 1 - Create a scatter plot and draw an informal inference about any correlation between the variables.
Objective 2 - Use a graphics calculator to find an equation for the least-squares line and use it to make predictions or estimates.

Lesson 6 - Introduction to Solving Equations
Objective 1 - Write and solve a linear equation in one variable.
Objective 2 - Solve a literal equation for a specified variable.

Lesson 7 - Introduction to Solving Inequalities
Objective 1 - Write, solve, and graph linear inequalities in one variable.
Objective 2 - Solve and graph compound linear inequalities in one variable.

Lesson 8 - Solving Absolute-Value Equations and Inequalities
Objective 1 - Write, solve, and graph absolute-value equations and inequalities in mathematical and real-world situations.

**Chapter 2 - Numbers and Functions**

Lesson 1 - Operations With Numbers
Objective 1 - Identify and use Properties of Real Numbers.
Objective 2 - Evaluate expressions using the order of operations.

Lesson 2 - Properties of Exponents
Objective 1 - Evaluate expressions involving exponents.
Objective 2 - Simplify expressions involving exponents.

Lesson 3 - Introduction to Functions
Objective 1 - State the domain and range of a relation, and tell whether it is a function.
Objective 2 - Write a function in function notation and evaluate it.

Lesson 4 - Operations With Functions
Objective 1 - Perform operations with functions to write new functions.
Objective 2 - Find the composition of two functions.

## Chapter 2 - Numbers and Functions (continued)

Lesson 5 - Inverses of Functions
Objective 1 - Find the inverse of a relation or function.
Objective 2 - Determine whether the inverse of a function is a function.
Lesson 6 - Special Functions
Objective 1 - Write, graph, and apply special functions: piecewise, step, and absolute value.
Lesson 7 - A Preview of Transformations
Objective 1 - Identify the transformation(s) from one function to another.

## Chapter 3 - Systems of Linear Equations and Inequalities

Lesson 1 - Solving Systems by Graphing or Substitution
Objective 1 - Solve a system of linear equations in two variables by graphing.
Objective 2 - Solve a system of linear equations by substitution.
Lesson 2 - Solving Systems by Elimination
Objective 1 - Solve a system of two linear equations in two variables by elimination.
Lesson 3 - Linear Inequalities in Two Variables
Objective 1 - Solve and graph a linear inequality in two variables.
Objective 2 - Use a linear inequality in two variables to solve real-world problems.
Lesson 4 - Systems of Linear Inequalities
Objective 1 - Write and graph a system of linear inequalities in two variables.
Objective 2 - Write a system of linear inequalities in two variables for a given solution region.
Lesson 5 - Linear Programming
Objective 1 - Write and graph a set of constraints for a linear-programming problem.
Objective 2 - Use linear programming to find the maximum or minimum value of an objective function.
Lesson 6 - Parametric Equations
Objective 1 - Graph a pair of parametric equations, and use them to model real-world applications.
Objective 2 - Write the function represented by a pair of parametric equations.

## Chapter 7 - Polynomial Functions (continued)

Lesson 5 - Zeros of Polynomial Functions

Objective 1 - Use the Rational Root Theorem and the Complex Conjugate Root Theorem to find the zeros of a polynomial function.

Objective 2 - Use the Fundamental Theorem to write a polynomial function given sufficient information about its zeros.

## Chapter 8 - Rational Functions & Radical Functions

Lesson 1 - Inverse, Joint, and Combined Variation

Objective 1 - Identify inverse, joint, and combined variations, find the constant of variation, and write an equation for the variation.

Objective 2 - Solve real-world problems involving inverse, joint, or combined variation.

Lesson 2 - Rational Functions and Their Graphs

Objective 1 - Identify and evaluate rational functions.

Objective 2 - Graph a rational function, find its domain, write equations for its asymptotes, and identify any holes in its graph.

Lesson 3 - Multiplying and Dividing Rational Expressions

Objective 1 - Multiply and divide rational expressions.

Objective 2 - Simplify rational expressions, including complex fractions.

Lesson 4 - Adding and Subtracting Rational Expressions

Objective 1 - Add and subtract rational expressions.

Lesson 5 - Solving Rational Equations and Inequalities

Objective 1 - Solve a rational equation or inequality by using algebra, a table, or a graph.

Objective 2 - Solve problems by using a rational equation or inequality.

Lesson 6 - Radical Expressions and Radical Functions

Objective 1 - Analyze the graphs of radical functions, and evaluate radical expressions.

Objective 2 - Find the inverse of a quadratic function.

Lesson 7 - Simplifying Radical Expressions

Objective 1 - Add, subtract, multiply, divide, and simplify radical expressions.

Objective 2 - Rationalize a denominator.

Lesson 8 - Solving Radical Equations and Inequalities

Objective 1 - Solve radical equations.

Objective 2 - Solve radical inequalities.

## Chapter 13 - Trigonometric Functions

Lesson 1 - Right-Triangle Trigonometry
Objective 1 - Find the trigonometric functions of acute angles.
Objective 2 - Solve a right triangle by using trigonometric functions.
Lesson 2 - Angles of Rotation
Objective 1 - Find coterminal and reference angles.
Objective 2 - Find the trigonometric function values of angles in standard position.
Lesson 3 - Trigonometric Functions of Any Angle
Objective 1 - Find exact values for trigonometric functions of special angles and their multiples.
Objective 2 - Find approximate values for trigonometric functions of any angle.
Lesson 4 - Radian Measure and Arc Length
Objective 1 - Convert from degree measure to radian measure and vice versa.
Objective 2 - Find arc length.
Lesson 5 - Graphing Trigonometric Functions
Objective 1 - Graph the sine, cosine, and tangent functions and their transformations.
Objective 2 - Use the sine function to solve problems.
Lesson 6 - Inverses of Trigonometric Functions
Objective 1 - Evaluate trigonometric expressions involving inverses.


## Chapter 14 - Further Topics in Trigonometry

Lesson 1 - The Law of Sines
Objective 1 - Solve mathematical and real-world problems by using the law of sines.
Lesson 2 - The Law of Cosines
Objective 1 - Use the law of cosines to solve triangles.
Lesson 3 - Fundamental Trigonometric Identities
Objective 1 - Prove fundamental trigonometric identities.
Objective 2 - Use fundamental trigonometric identities to rewrite expressions.
Lesson 4 - Sum and Difference Identities
Objective 1 - Evaluate expressions by using the sum and difference identities.
Objective 2 - Use matrix multiplication with sum and difference identities to perform rotations.
Lesson 5 - Double-Angle and Half-Angle Identities
Objective 1 - Evaluate and simplify expressions by using double-angle and half-angle identities.
Lesson 6 - Solving Trigonometric Equations
Objective 1 - Solve trigonometric equations algebraically and graphically.
Objective 2 - Solve real-world problems by using trigonometric equations.

**Lesson 1:  Tables and Graphs of Linear Equations**

Objective 1:  Represent a real-world linear relationship in a table, graph, or equation.

[1.1.1.1]  *Dynamic Item*

1.  The cost of a school banquet is $65 plus $14 for each person attending. Determine the equation that models this problem. What is the cost for 45 people?

[A] $y = 14x + 65$; $695

[B] $y = 14x - 65$; $565

[C] $y = 65x + 14$; $2,939

[D] $y = 65x - 14$; $2,911

[1.1.1.2]  *Dynamic Item*

2.  Model the following situation with an equation and a graph:
    An amusement park charges $13.00 admission and $2.00 per ride.

[A]     $y = 2x + 13$

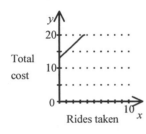

[B]     $y = -2x + 13$

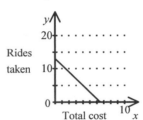

[C]     $y = -2x + 13$

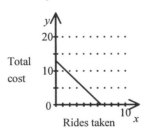

[D]  none of these

[1.1.1.3]  *Dynamic Item*

3.  Hans pays $377 in advance on his account at the athletic club. Each time he uses the club, $5 is deducted from the account. Write an equation that represents the value remaining in his account after $x$ visits to the club. Find the value remaining in the account after 8 visits.

**Lesson 1: Tables and Graphs of Linear Equations**

[1.1.1.4] *Dynamic Item*

4. Abbiville is a small town that has been steadily growing since 1960. Use the table below to create a linear equation that estimates Abbiville's population over time. What will the population be in 2017 if the growth remains constant?

| Year | 1960 | 1970 | 1980 | 1990 | 2000 |
|------------|------|------|------|------|------|
| Population | 10 | 33 | 57 | 80 | 103 |

Objective 2: Identify linear equations and linear relationships between variables in a table.

[1.1.2.5] *Dynamic Item*

5. Which equation and graph fit the data in the table?

| $x$ | $-2$ | $-1$ | 0 | 1 | 2 |
|-----|------|------|---|----|----|
| $y$ | $-11$ | $-3$ | 5 | 13 | 21 |

[A] $y = 8x + 5$

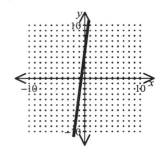

[B] $y = -8x - 5$

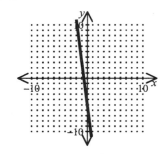

[C] $y = -8x + 5$

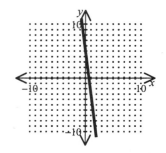

[D] $y = 8x - 5$

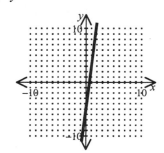

**Lesson 1: Tables and Graphs of Linear Equations**

[1.1.2.6] *Dynamic Item*

6. Graph the equation $y = \frac{7}{2}x + 3$.

[A]

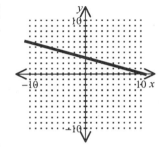

[B]

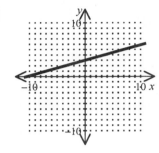

[C]

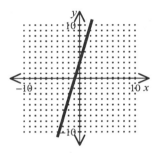

[D]

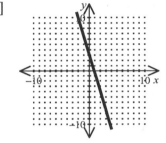

[1.1.2.7] *Dynamic Item*

7. State whether the equation $y = 9x^2 - 11$ is linear.

[1.1.2.8] *Dynamic Item*

8. Complete the table. Then graph the line.
   $y = x - 4$

   | $x$ | $y$ |
   | --- | --- |
   | $-2$ | |
   | 0 | |
   | 4 | |
   | 5 | |

**Lesson 2:  Slopes and Intercepts**

Objective 1:  Graph a linear equation.

[1.2.1.9]  *Dynamic Item*

9.  Which is the equation of the line with slope 3 and $y$-intercept $-4$?

   [A]  $3x + y - 4 = 0$     [B]  $-3x - y + 4 = 0$     [C]  $-3x + y - 4 = 0$     [D]  $3x - y - 4 = 0$

[1.2.1.10]  *Dynamic Item*

10.  Write an equation for a line with slope $m = -\dfrac{4}{5}$ and $y$-intercept $b = 2$. Then draw the graph of the equation.

   [A]  $y = x + 2$

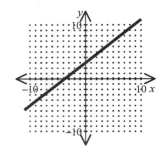

   [B]  $y = -\dfrac{4}{5}x + 2$

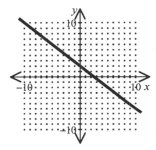

   [C]  $x = -\dfrac{4}{5}y + 2$

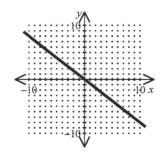

   [D]  $-\dfrac{4}{5}y = x + 2$

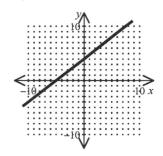

[1.2.1.11]  *Dynamic Item*

11.  Find the slope and the $y$-intercept of the line $6x - 2y = 4$.

**Lesson 2:  Slopes and Intercepts**

[1.2.1.12]  *Dynamic Item*

12.   Use the slope and *y*-intercept to graph  $y = 4x - 7$.

Objective 2:  Write a linear equation for a given line in the coordinate plane.

[1.2.2.13]  *Dynamic Item*

13.   Which equation best describes the graph below?

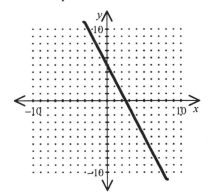

[A]  $y = -2x + 5$      [B]  $y = -\dfrac{1}{2}x + 5$      [C]  $y = -2x + \dfrac{5}{2}$      [D]  $y = \dfrac{1}{2}x + 5$

**Lesson 2: Slopes and Intercepts**

[1.2.2.14] *Dynamic Item*

14. Match the equation $y = 0.05x - 3$ with its graph.

[A]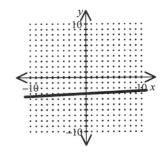

[B]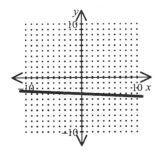

[C]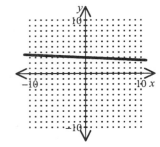

[D]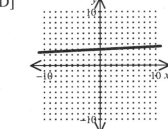

[1.2.2.15] *Dynamic Item*

15. Write an equation that best describes the graph below.

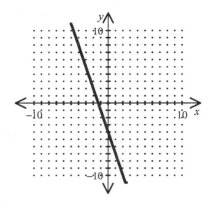

**Lesson 2: Slopes and Intercepts**

[1.2.2.16] *Dynamic Item*

16. Use the table and graph to write a linear equation.

| $x$ | $-2$ | $-1$ | 0 | 1 | 2 |
|---|---|---|---|---|---|
| $y$ | 19 | 14 | 9 | 4 | $-1$ |

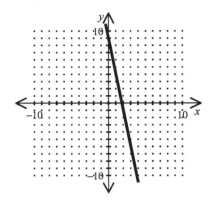

**Lesson 3: Linear Equations in Two Variables**

Objective 1: Write a linear equation in two variables given sufficient information.

[1.3.1.17] *Dynamic Item*

17. Write the slope-intercept form of an equation of the line that passes through the point $(1, -6)$ and has the slope $m = -4$.

   [A] $y = 4x - 2$      [B] $y = -4x - 6$      [C] $y = -4x - 2$      [D] $y = 4x - 6$

[1.3.1.18] *Dynamic Item*

18. Write an equation in slope-intercept form for a line that passes through the given pair of points.
   $(-7, -2), (1, 5)$

   [A] $y = \frac{7}{8}x + \frac{33}{8}$      [B] $y = \frac{8}{7}x - \frac{33}{8}$      [C] $y = \frac{7}{8}x + \frac{8}{33}$      [D] $y = -\frac{8}{7}x - \frac{8}{33}$

**Lesson 3:  Linear Equations in Two Variables**

[1.3.1.19]  *Dynamic Item*

19.  Write an equation in slope-intercept form for a line that passes through the given pair of points.

$(-1, 6), \ (-5, -3)$

[1.3.1.20]  *Dynamic Item*

20.  Write the slope-intercept form of an equation of the line that passes through the point $(-5, 1)$ and has the slope $m = -7$.

Objective 2:  Write an equation for a line that is parallel or perpendicular to a given line.

[1.3.2.21]  *Dynamic Item*

21.  Which is the equation of the line passing through the point $(5, -3)$ and perpendicular to the line $y = 5x + 2$?

[A]  $5x + y - 22 = 0$             [B]  $x + 5y + 10 = 0$

[C]  $-x - 5y + 10 = 0$       [D]  $-5x - y + 22 = 0$

[1.3.2.22]  *Dynamic Item*

22.  Find the slope-intercept form of the line passing through the point $(7, -3)$ and parallel to the line $-6x - 9y = -2$.

[A]  $y = -\dfrac{3}{2}x - \dfrac{3}{5}$     [B]  $y = -\dfrac{2}{3}x + \dfrac{5}{3}$     [C]  $y = \dfrac{2}{3}x + \dfrac{5}{3}$     [D]  $y = -\dfrac{2}{3}x - \dfrac{3}{5}$

[1.3.2.23]  *Dynamic Item*

23.  Write an equation in slope-intercept form of the line that passes through $(0, \ 1)$ and is parallel to the graph of $y = -3x - 4$.

**Lesson 3:  Linear Equations in Two Variables**

[1.3.2.24]  *Dynamic Item*

24.  Write the equation of the line, in slope-intercept form, that contains the point $(7, -8)$ and is perpendicular to the line $5x - 6y = -9$.

**Lesson 4:  Direct Variation and Proportion**

Objective 1:  Write and apply direct-variation equations.

[1.4.1.25]  *Dynamic Item*

25.  A new Internet company is selling more software packages each day it is in business. From the data in the table, write a model relating the number of days in business and the total units sold. Estimate the number of units sold after 90 days in business.

| Days in business, $x$ | 50 | 60 | 70 | 80 |
|---|---|---|---|---|
| Units sold, $y$ | 15 | 18 | 21 | 24 |

[A]  $y = \dfrac{10}{3}x$;  300 units

[B]  $y = \dfrac{10}{3}x$;  30 units

[C]  $y = 0.3x$;  30 units

[D]  $y = 0.3x$;  27 units

[1.4.1.26]  *Dynamic Item*

26.  If $x = 38$ when $y = 190$ and $x$ varies directly as $y$, then find $x$ when $y = 140$.

[A] 38  [B] 28  [C] 23  [D] 18

[1.4.1.27]  *Dynamic Item*

27.  Tell whether the data show direct variation. If so, give the constant of variation and write the equation.

| Days | 1 | 4 | 10 | 13 |
|---|---|---|---|---|
| Growth (cm) | 1.25 | 5 | 12.5 | 16.25 |

**Lesson 4: Direct Variation and Proportion**

[1.4.1.28] *Dynamic Item*

28. Write the variation equation and find the quantity indicated. $x$ varies directly as $y$. If $x$ is 49 when $y$ is 70, find $x$ when $y$ is 30.

Objective 2: Write and solve proportions.

[1.4.2.29] *Dynamic Item*

29. Solve the proportion $\dfrac{x+2}{3} = \dfrac{2}{9}$.     [A] $-\dfrac{4}{3}$     [B] $\dfrac{8}{3}$     [C] $-12$     [D] $-\dfrac{3}{4}$

[1.4.2.30] *Dynamic Item*

30. Write a proportion that models the statement 30 is to $x$ as 35 is to 7.

    [A] $\dfrac{30}{7} = \dfrac{x}{35}$     [B] $\dfrac{30}{x} = \dfrac{7}{35}$     [C] $\dfrac{30}{x} = \dfrac{35}{7}$     [D] $\dfrac{30}{x} = \dfrac{35}{x}$

[1.4.2.31] *Dynamic Item*

31. A survey indicated that 5 out of 8 doctors used brand X aspirin. If 3200 doctors were surveyed, write a proportion which could be used to find how many doctors, $D$, used brand X.

[1.4.2.32] *Dynamic Item*

32. Solve the proportion $\dfrac{5}{6} = \dfrac{y}{126}$.

**Lesson 5:  Scatter Plots and Least-Squares Lines**

Objective 1:  Create a scatter plot and draw an informal inference about any correlation between the variables.

[1.5.1.33]  *Dynamic Item*

33.  A mail service clerk kept track of the number of large packages, and the time of day the package was shipped. The data is displayed below.

| packages | 9 | 0 | 10 | 0 | 5 | 10 | 1 | 5 |
|---|---|---|---|---|---|---|---|---|
| time of day | 2 p.m. | 3 p.m. | 4 p.m. | 5 p.m. | 6 p.m. | 7 p.m. | 8 p.m. | 9 p.m. |

If the data were displayed on a scatter plot, could the correlation of the data be represented by a linear model? If there is a linear correlation, is there a positive or negative correlation?

[A]  The data have no reliable correlation.

[B]  It is a linear model with a positive correlation.

[C]  It is not a linear model.        [D]  It is a linear model with a negative correlation.

[1.5.1.34]  *Dynamic Item*

34.  A police dispatcher kept track of the number of emergency calls received while they were on duty, and the time of day each call was received. The data is displayed below.

| emergency calls | 5 | 10 | 0 | 5 | 10 | 5 | 9 |
|---|---|---|---|---|---|---|---|
| time of day | 10 a.m. | 11 a.m. | Noon | 1 p.m. | 2 p.m. | 3 p.m. | 4 p.m. |

If the data were displayed on a scatter plot, could the correlation of the data be represented by a linear model? If there is a linear correlation, is there a positive or negative correlation?

[A]  It is a linear model with a positive correlation.

[B]  The data have no reliable correlation.

[C]  It is a linear model with a negative correlation.    [D]  none of these

**Lesson 5: Scatter Plots and Least-Squares Lines**

[1.5.1.35] *Dynamic Item*

35. A foreman on an automobile assembly line kept track of the number of defects reported by workers, and the time of day each defect was reported. The data is displayed below.

| defects | 7 | 7 | 5 | 5 | 4 | 4 | 2 | 2 |
|---|---|---|---|---|---|---|---|---|
| time of day | 9 a.m. | 10 a.m. | 11 a.m. | Noon | 1 p.m. | 2 p.m. | 3 p.m. | 4 p.m. |

Display the data on a scatter plot, and determine whether the correlation of the data can be represented by a linear model. If there is a linear correlation, is there a positive or negative correlation?

[1.5.1.36] *Dynamic Item*

36. A technician at the local oil change shop kept track of the number of cars that received an oil change during the day, and the time of day the cars were serviced. The data is displayed below.

| oil changes | 3 | 3 | 5 | 4 | 6 | 7 | 6 |
|---|---|---|---|---|---|---|---|
| time of day | 10 a.m. | 11 a.m. | Noon | 1 p.m. | 2 p.m. | 3 p.m. | 4 p.m. |

Display the data on a scatter plot, and determine whether the correlation of the data can be represented by a linear model. If there is a linear correlation, is there a positive or negative correlation?

Objective 2: Use a graphic calculator to find an equation for the least-squares line and use it to make predictions or estimates.

[1.5.2.37] *Dynamic Item*

37. For the data given, find the equation of the line of best fit.

| $x$ | 3 | 4 | 5 | 8 | 10 |
|---|---|---|---|---|---|
| $y$ | 2 | 3 | 7 | 8 | 7 |

[A] $y = 0.766x + 0.99$          [B] $y = 0.74x + 0.99$

[C] $y = 0.74x + 1.65$          [D] $y = 0.766x + 1.65$

**Lesson 5: Scatter Plots and Least-Squares Lines**

[1.5.2.38] *Dynamic Item*

38. The following table shows the results of an experiment to determine if there is a relationship between the number of hours of television watched ($H$) and the GPA ($G$) of students in high school. Use a graphing calculator to find the equation of the line which best fits the data and gives the GPA as a function of the number of hours of television watched $(G = mH + b)$.

    Also, find the correlation coefficient for this data and discuss whether or not the line is a good model for the data.

| GPA ($G$) | 4 | 3.5 | 2 | 3.3 | 2.6 |
|---|---|---|---|---|---|
| Hours of TV ($H$) | 1.3 | 1.4 | 2.5 | 1.5 | 1.9 |

[A] $G = -0.607H + 3.589$, −0.969, a good model

[B] $G = -1.548H + 5.742$, −1.548, not a good model

[C] $G = -0.607H + 3.589$, −0.607, not a good model

[D] $G = -1.548H + 5.742$, −0.969, a good model

[1.5.2.39] *Dynamic Item*

39. For the data given, approximate the equation of the line of best fit.

| $x$ | 1 | 2 | 7 | 8 | 10 |
|---|---|---|---|---|---|
| $y$ | 4 | 3 | 4 | 6 | 7 |

**Lesson 5: Scatter Plots and Least-Squares Lines**

[1.5.2.40] *Dynamic Item*

40. The following table shows the results of an experiment to determine if there is a relationship between the number of hours of television watched ($H$) per day and the average number of books read ($B$) per month by students in high school. Use a graphing calculator to find the equation of the line that best fits the data and gives the average number of books read as a function of the number of hours of television watched $(B = mH + b)$. Also, find the correlation coefficient for this data and discuss whether or not the line is a good model for the data.

| Number of Books ($B$) | 3.8 | 3.6 | 2.2 | 3.1 | 2.8 |
|---|---|---|---|---|---|
| Hours of TV ($H$) | 1.1 | 1.1 | 1.8 | 1.3 | 1.4 |

**Lesson 6: Introduction to Solving Equations**

Objective 1: Write and solve a linear equation in one variable.

[1.6.1.41] *Dynamic Item*

41. Solve for $x$.     [A] $x = -5$     [B] $x = -3$     [C] $x = 5$     [D] $x = 3$
    $x + 4 = -1$

[1.6.1.42] *Dynamic Item*

42. Solve for $x$.     [A] $x = 4$     [B] $x = -4$     [C] $x = -6$     [D] $x = 6$
    $3x - 6 = x + 6$

[1.6.1.43] *Dynamic Item*

43. Solve for $x$.
    $x - \dfrac{1}{3} = \dfrac{1}{15}$

[1.6.1.44] *Dynamic Item*

44. Solve for $x$.
    $4x + 6 = x + 4$

**Lesson 6:  Introduction to Solving Equations**

Objective 2:  Solve a literal equation for a specified variable.

[1.6.2.45]  *Dynamic Item*

45.   Solve the equation or formula for the variable specified.
$A = 2c^2 + d$ , for $d$

[A]  $d = \dfrac{A}{2c^2}$        [B]  $d = A - 2c^2$        [C]  $d = \dfrac{2c^2}{A}$        [D]  $d = 2c^2 - A$

[1.6.2.46]  *Dynamic Item*

46.   Solve the equation or formula for the variable specified.
$B = \dfrac{7}{8}(A - 10)$, for $A$

[A]  $A = \dfrac{8B + 80}{7}$     [B]  $A = \dfrac{8B + 70}{7}$     [C]  $A = \dfrac{8B + 73}{8}$     [D]  $A = \dfrac{8B + 63}{8}$

[1.6.2.47]  *Dynamic Item*

47.   Solve the equation or formula for the variable specified.
$-7 = t + 9s$, for $s$

[1.6.2.48]  *Dynamic Item*

48.   Solve the equation or formula for the variable specified.
$F = kma$,  for $a$

**Lesson 7: Introduction to Solving Inequalities**

Objective 1: Write, solve, and graph linear inequalities in one variable.

[1.7.1.49] *Dynamic Item*

49. Solve the inequality $4x - 1 \geq 2(x - 1)$ and check your solution. Graph the solution on a number line.

[A] $x < -0.5$

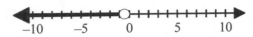

[B] $x \geq -0.5$

[C] $x \leq -0.5$

[D] $x > -0.5$

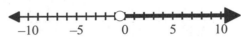

[1.7.1.50] *Dynamic Item*

50. Which inequality has the solution shown in the graph?

[A] $m + 7 < 5$      [B] $m + 7 \geq 5$      [C] $m + 7 \leq 5$      [D] $m + 7 > 5$

[1.7.1.51] *Dynamic Item*

51. What inequality describes the graph?

**Lesson 7: Introduction to Solving Inequalities**

[1.7.1.52] *Dynamic Item*

52. Solve the inequality $5x - 3 \leq 3(x - 2)$ and check your solution. Graph the solution on a number line.

Objective 2: Solve and graph compound linear inequalities in one variable.

[1.7.2.53] *Dynamic Item*

53. Solve the compound inequality. Then graph the solution on a number line.
    $x + 3 > -3$ and $x \leq 4$

[A] $x \leq -6$ or $x > 4$          [B] $-6 < x \leq 4$

[C] $-6 \leq x < 4$          [D] $x < -6$ or $x \geq 4$

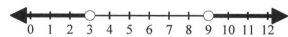

[1.7.2.54] *Dynamic Item*

54. Solve the compound inequality. Then graph the solution on a number line.
    $2x - 2 > 4$ and $4x + 4 < 40$

[A] $\varnothing$

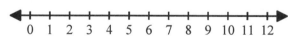

[B] $x$ is any real number.

[C] $3 < x < 9$

[D] $x < 3$ or $x > 9$

**Lesson 7: Introduction to Solving Inequalities**

[1.7.2.55]  *Dynamic Item*

55.  Solve the compound inequality. Then graph the solution on a number line.
$2x + 3 > -9$ and $5x + 1 < 1$

[1.7.2.56]  *Dynamic Item*

56.  Solve the compound inequality. Then graph the solution on a number line.
$x + 2 \leq -2$  or  $x > 5$

**Lesson 8: Solving Absolute-Value Equations and Inequalities**

Objective 1:  Write, solve, and graph absolute-value equations and inequalities in mathematical and real-world situations.

[1.8.1.57]  *Dynamic Item*

57.  Solve the equation: $|2x - 4| = 2$

[A] $x = 2$, or $x = 1$     [B] $x = 3$, or $x = 1$     [C] $x = -3$, or $x = 1$     [D] $x = -5$, or $x = 1$

[1.8.1.58]  *Dynamic Item*

58.  When Spheres-R-Us ships bags of golf balls, each bag must be within 6 balls of 410. Identify the inequality which results in an acceptable number of golf balls in each bag.

[A] $|b - 6| \leq 410$      [B] $|410 - b| \leq 6$      [C] $|410 - 6| \leq b$      [D] $|6 - b| \leq 410$

[1.8.1.59]  *Dynamic Item*

59.  Solve the inequality: $|2x + 4| > 6$

[1.8.1.60]  *Dynamic Item*

60.  The water temperature for a manufacturing process should be kept at $160°\,\text{F}$. A computer program uses the inequality $|t - 160| < 20$, which describes the acceptable water temperatures, $t$, in degrees. What is the range of acceptable temperatures for the water?

**Lesson 1: Tables and Graphs of Linear Equations**

Objective 1: Represent a real-world linear relationship in a table, graph, or equation.

[1.1.1.1] *Dynamic Item*

[1]  [A]

[1.1.1.2] *Dynamic Item*

[2]  [A]

[1.1.1.3] *Dynamic Item*

[3]  $V = 377 - 5x$; $337

[1.1.1.4] *Dynamic Item*

[4]  143 people

Objective 2: Identify linear equations and linear relationships between variables in a table.

[1.1.2.5] *Dynamic Item*

[5]  [A]

[1.1.2.6] *Dynamic Item*

[6]  [C]

[1.1.2.7] *Dynamic Item*

[7]  not linear

[1.1.2.8] *Dynamic Item*

| x  | y  |
|----|----|
| −2 | −6 |
| 0  | −4 |
| 4  | 0  |
| 5  | 1  |

[8] _____

**Lesson 2: Slopes and Intercepts**

Objective 1: Graph a linear equation.

[1.2.1.9] *Dynamic Item*

[9] [D]____

[1.2.1.10] *Dynamic Item*

[10] [B]____

[1.2.1.11] *Dynamic Item*

[11] $m = 3, \ b = -2$ _____

[1.2.1.12]  *Dynamic Item*

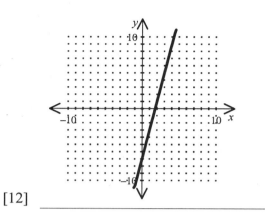

[12]  _____

Objective 2:  Write a linear equation for a given line in the coordinate plane.

[1.2.2.13]  *Dynamic Item*

[13]  [A]  _____

[1.2.2.14]  *Dynamic Item*

[14]  [A]  _____

[1.2.2.15]  *Dynamic Item*

[15]  $y = -3x - 4$  _____

[1.2.2.16]  *Dynamic Item*

[16]  $y = -5x + 9$  _____

**Lesson 3:  Linear Equations in Two Variables**

Objective 1:  Write a linear equation in two variables given sufficient information.

[1.3.1.17]  *Dynamic Item*

[17]  [C]  _____

[1.3.1.18] *Dynamic Item*

[18]  [A]

[1.3.1.19] *Dynamic Item*

[19]  $y = \dfrac{9}{4}x + \dfrac{33}{4}$

[1.3.1.20] *Dynamic Item*

[20]  $y = -7x - 34$

Objective 2: Write an equation for a line that is parallel or perpendicular to a given line.

[1.3.2.21] *Dynamic Item*

[21]  [B]

[1.3.2.22] *Dynamic Item*

[22]  [B]

[1.3.2.23] *Dynamic Item*

[23]  $y = -3x + 1$

[1.3.2.24] *Dynamic Item*

[24]  $y = -\dfrac{6}{5}x + \dfrac{2}{5}$

**Lesson 4:  Direct Variation and Proportion**

Objective 1: Write and apply direct-variation equations.

[1.4.1.25] *Dynamic Item*

[25]  [D]

[1.4.1.26] *Dynamic Item*

[26]  [B]

[1.4.1.27] *Dynamic Item*

[27]  The data show direct variation; 1.25; $g = 1.25d$

[1.4.1.28] *Dynamic Item*

[28]  $x = ky$; 21

Objective 2:  Write and solve proportions.

[1.4.2.29] *Dynamic Item*

[29]  [A]

[1.4.2.30] *Dynamic Item*

[30]  [C]

[1.4.2.31] *Dynamic Item*

[31]  $\dfrac{5}{8} = \dfrac{D}{3200}$

[1.4.2.32] *Dynamic Item*

[32]  105

**Lesson 5:  Scatter Plots and Least-Squares Lines**

Objective 1:  Create a scatter plot and draw an informal inference about any correlation between the variables.

[1.5.1.33] *Dynamic Item*

[33]  [A]

---

[1.5.1.34]  *Dynamic Item*

[34]  [B]

[1.5.1.35]  *Dynamic Item*

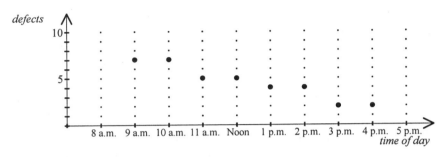

[35]  It is a linear model with a negative correlation.

[1.5.1.36]  *Dynamic Item*

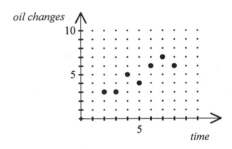

[36]  It is a linear model with a positive correlation.

Objective 2:  Use a graphic calculator to find an equation for the least-squares line and use it to make predictions or estimates.

[1.5.2.37]  *Dynamic Item*

[37]  [B]

[1.5.2.38]  *Dynamic Item*

[38]  [D]

[1.5.2.39]  *Dynamic Item*

[39]   $y = 0.4x + 2.82$

[1.5.2.40]  *Dynamic Item*

[40]   $B = -2.169H + 6.006$, $-0.976$, a good model

**Lesson 6:  Introduction to Solving Equations**

Objective 1:  Write and solve a linear equation in one variable.

[1.6.1.41]  *Dynamic Item*

[41]   [A]

[1.6.1.42]  *Dynamic Item*

[42]   [D]

[1.6.1.43]  *Dynamic Item*

[43]   $x = \dfrac{2}{5}$

[1.6.1.44]  *Dynamic Item*

[44]   $x = -\dfrac{2}{3}$

Objective 2:  Solve a literal equation for a specified variable.

[1.6.2.45]  *Dynamic Item*

[45]   [B]

[1.6.2.46]  *Dynamic Item*

[46]   [B]

Algebra 2

[1.6.2.47] *Dynamic Item*

[47] $s = \dfrac{-7 - t}{9}$

[1.6.2.48] *Dynamic Item*

[48] $a = \dfrac{F}{km}$

**Lesson 7: Introduction to Solving Inequalities**

Objective 1: Write, solve, and graph linear inequalities in one variable.

[1.7.1.49] *Dynamic Item*

[49] [B]

[1.7.1.50] *Dynamic Item*

[50] [D]

[1.7.1.51] *Dynamic Item*

[51] $x \geq 5$

[1.7.1.52] *Dynamic Item*

$x \leq -1.5$

[52]

Objective 2: Solve and graph compound linear inequalities in one variable.

[1.7.2.53] *Dynamic Item*

[53] [B]

[1.7.2.54]  *Dynamic Item*

[54]  [C]

[1.7.2.55]  *Dynamic Item*

$-6 < x < 0$

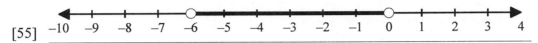

[55]

[1.7.2.56]  *Dynamic Item*

$x \leq -4$ or $x > 5$

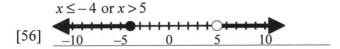

[56]

**Lesson 8: Solving Absolute-Value Equations and Inequalities**

Objective 1:  Write, solve, and graph absolute-value equations and inequalities in mathematical and real-world situations.

[1.8.1.57]  *Dynamic Item*

[57]  [B]

[1.8.1.58]  *Dynamic Item*

[58]  [B]

[1.8.1.59]  *Dynamic Item*

[59]  $x > 1$ or $x < -5$

[1.8.1.60]  *Dynamic Item*

[60]  $140°\,F < t < 180°\,F$

**Lesson 1: Operations With Numbers**

Objective 1: Identify and use Properties of Real Numbers.

[2.1.1.1] *Dynamic Item*

1. Which property is shown by the following statement?
   $5 \times (4+11) = 5 \times 4 + 5 \times 11$

   [A] The Associative Property of Multiplication

   [B] The Identity Property of Addition

   [C] The Distributive Property          [D] The Identity Property of Multiplication

[2.1.1.2] *Dynamic Item*

2. Which of the following is an example of the Commutative Property of Addition?

   [A] $1+2 = 3+0$                    [B] $2+5 = 5+2$

   [C] $4+(2+2) = 4+(2+2)$            [D] $(6+9)+2 = 6+(9+2)$

[2.1.1.3] *Dynamic Item*

3. What property is shown below?
   $6 \times (2 \times 8) = (6 \times 2) \times 8$

[2.1.1.4] *Dynamic Item*

4. Identify the algebraic properties that justify the equivalence of the following pairs of algebraic expressions.
   a. $(2a + 6b) + 3c = 2a + (6b + 3c)$
   b. $7(2 - 6t) = 14 - 42t$
   c. $(4a + 6b)2c = (6b + 4a)2c$
   d. $3y + 7y = (3+7)y$

**Lesson 1: Operations With Numbers**

Objective 2: Evaluate expressions using the order of operations.

[2.1.2.5]  *Dynamic Item*

5.  Evaluate the expression.      [A] 11        [B] −11        [C] −8        [D] 14
    $6 - 14 \cdot 2 \div 7 + 9$

[2.1.2.6]  *Dynamic Item*

6.  Evaluate the expression.      [A] 343       [B] 5975       [C] 143        [D] 272
    $27 \times 3^2 - 4 \cdot 5^2$

[2.1.2.7]  *Dynamic Item*

7.  Evaluate the expression.
    $5 - 16 \cdot 6 \div 8 + 4$

[2.1.2.8]  *Dynamic Item*

8.  Evaluate the expression.
    $$\frac{64 \cdot 4^2 - 4 \cdot 7^2}{7 + 4^2}$$

**Lesson 2: Properties of Exponents**

Objective 1: Evaluate expressions involving exponents.

[2.2.1.9]  *Dynamic Item*

9.  Evaluate the expression.      [A] $\frac{1}{24}$       [B] $\frac{1}{64}$       [C] 24        [D] 64
    $(16)^{\frac{3}{2}}$

**Lesson 2: Properties of Exponents**

[2.2.1.10] *Dynamic Item*

10. Evaluate the expression.     [A] $\dfrac{64}{9}$     [B] $\dfrac{9}{64}$     [C] $\dfrac{9}{8}$     [D] $\dfrac{3}{4}$

$\left(\dfrac{3}{8}\right)^2$

[2.2.1.11] *Dynamic Item*

11. Evaluate the expression.

$\left(-\dfrac{1}{4}\right)^{-3}$

[2.2.1.12] *Dynamic Item*

12. Evaluate the expression.

$(7)^{-2}$

Objective 2: Simplify expressions involving exponents.

[2.2.2.13] *Dynamic Item*

13. Simplify the expression.     [A] $-\dfrac{1}{x}$     [B] $\dfrac{1}{x^{12}}$     [C] $x^2$     [D] $-x^{-12}$

$\dfrac{(-x)^3(-x^7)^4}{(x^4)^8}$

[2.2.2.14] *Dynamic Item*

14. Simplify the expression.

$\left(\dfrac{-5a^2b^2c^0}{3a^4b^5c^5}\right)^{-3}$

[A] $-\dfrac{3^3b^9c^{15}}{5^3a^6}$     [B] $-\dfrac{3^3a^6b^9c^{15}}{5^3}$     [C] $\dfrac{5^3a^6}{3^3b^9c^{15}}$     [D] $\dfrac{3^3a^6}{5^3b^9c^{15}}$

**Lesson 2: Properties of Exponents**

[2.2.2.15] *Dynamic Item*

15. Simplify the expression.
$$4x^6\left(6x^3\right)$$

[2.2.2.16] *Dynamic Item*

16. Simplify the expression.
$$\frac{\left(x^2y^{12}\right)\left(x^4y\right)}{\left(x^3y^2\right)^5}$$

**Lesson 3: Introduction to Functions**

Objective 1: State the domain and range of a relation, and tell whether it is a function.

[2.3.1.17] *Dynamic Item*

17. Determine which relation is a function with the correct domain and range.

[A]

| $x$ | $y$ |
|-----|-----|
| $-8$ | 5 |
| $-7$ | 2 |
| $-6$ | 1 |

domain:$=\{-8, -7, -6\}$
range:$\{5, 2, 1\}$

[B] $\{(4, 5), (7, 9), (7, 8), (8, 8)\}$
domain:$\{4, 7, 8\}$
range:$\{5, 9, 8\}$

[C] $\{(4, 5), (4, 9), (6, 8), (8, 7)\}$
domain:$\{4, 6, 8\}$
range:$\{5, 9, 8, 7\}$

[D] $\{(4, 7), (6, 8), (6, 5), (4, 8)\}$
domain:$\{7, 8, 5, 4\}$
range:$\{4, 6, 8\}$

**Lesson 3: Introduction to Functions**

[2.3.1.18]  *Dynamic Item*

18. Determine which relation is a function with the correct domain and range.

[A]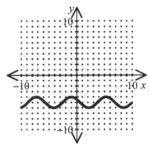

domain: $-6 \leq y \leq -4$
range: all real numbers

[B]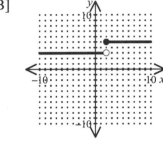

domain: all real numbers
range: $\{3, 5\}$

[C]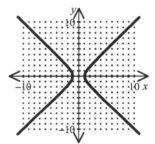

domain: $x \leq -1$ or $x \geq 1$
range: all real numbers

[D]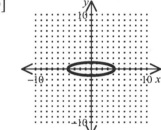

domain: $-1 \leq y \leq 1$
range: $-4 \leq x \leq 4$

[2.3.1.19]  *Dynamic Item*

19. Determine whether the relation is a function and state the domain and the range.

| $x$ | $y$ |
|-----|-----|
| $-6$ | 8 |
| $-5$ | 6 |
| $-6$ | 4 |

**Lesson 3: Introduction to Functions**

[2.3.1.20] *Dynamic Item*

20. Determine whether the relation is a function and state the domain and the range.

| x | y |
|----|----|
| 15 | 13 |
| 13 | 15 |
| 18 | 12 |
| 18 | 12 |

Objective 2: Write a function in function notation and evaluate it.

[2.3.2.21] *Dynamic Item*

21. A T-shirt company estimates that the average cost per shirt can be approximated by the function $A(x) = \dfrac{4.25x + 150}{x}$, where $x$ is the number of T-shirts made. Find the average cost per T-shirt when the company makes 10 shirts.

[A] $19.25      [B] $5.75      [C] $15.43      [D] $4.27

[2.3.2.22] *Dynamic Item*

22. Ricardo Morris plans to decorate T-shirts to sell at a crafts fair. The decorations cost $33.00 and the T-shirts cost $4.25 each.
a. Write a function expressing the cost, $C(x)$, of the project in terms of the number of T-shirts decorated, $x$.
b. Determine the cost of decorating 60 T-shirts.
c. How many T-shirts can be decorated with a budget of $330.50?

[A] a. $C(x) = 33.00x + 4.25$
    b. $1984.25
    c. 72

[B] a. $C(x) = 4.25x + 33.00$
    b. $288.00
    c. 70

[C] a. $C(x) = 4.25x$
    b. $255.00
    c. 71

[D] a. $C(x) = 4.25 + 33.00$
    b. $37.25
    c. 73

**Lesson 3: Introduction to Functions**

[2.3.2.23] *Dynamic Item*

23. Since 1993, Ian Glaser has owned a franchise of take-out restaurants called Paolo's Pizza. The number of customers, $C$, in thousands, that Paolo's Pizza has served each year can be modeled by the function $C(t) = t^2 + 33t + 500$, where $t$ is the number of years from 1993. Using this model, estimate the number of customers served in 1995.

[2.3.2.24] *Dynamic Item*

24. Tariq Aziz plans to decorate dolls to sell at a crafts fair. The decorations cost $26.50 and the dolls cost $6.75 each.
a. Write a function expressing the cost, $C(x)$, of the project in terms of the number of dolls decorated, $x$.
b. Determine the cost of decorating 25 dolls.
c. How many dolls can be decorated with a budget of $262.75?

**Lesson 4: Operations With Functions**

Objective 1: Perform operations with functions to write new functions.

[2.4.1.25] *Dynamic Item*

25. If $f(x) = 9 - x^2$ and $g(x) = 3 - x$, which is the rule of function $\dfrac{f}{g}(x)$?

[A] $x^3 - 3x^2 - 9x + 27$     [B] $-x^2 + x + 6$     [C] $3 + x$     [D] $-x^2 - x + 12$

[2.4.1.26] *Dynamic Item*

26. If $f(x) = 49 - x^2$ and $g(x) = 7 - x$, which is the rule of the function $(f + g)(x)$?

[A] $7 + x$     [B] $-x^2 - x + 56$     [C] $x^3 - 7x^2 - 49x + 343$     [D] $-x^2 + x + 42$

[2.4.1.27] *Dynamic Item*

27. If $f(x) = 4 - x^2$ and $g(x) = 2 - x$, find the rule of the function $(f + g)(x)$.

**Lesson 4: Operations With Functions**

[2.4.1.28] *Dynamic Item*

28. If $f(x) = 2x^2 + 3$ and $g(x) = -4 + x^2$, find the rule of the function $3f(x) - 3g(x)$.

Objective 2: Find the composition of two functions.

[2.4.2.29] *Dynamic Item*

29. For the pair of functions, $f$ and $g$, find $(f \circ g)(x)$ and $(g \circ f)(x)$.
    $f(x) = 5 - 6x, \quad g(x) = 3x + 4$

    [A] $(f \circ g)(x) = -18x - 19$          [B] $(f \circ g)(x) = -3x + 9$
         $(g \circ f)(x) = -18x + 19$              $(g \circ f)(x) = -18x - 19$

    [C] $(f \circ g)(x) = 3x - 9$            [D] $(f \circ g)(x) = 18x + 19$
         $(g \circ f)(x) = 18x - 19$               $(g \circ f)(x) = -3x + 9$

## Lesson 4: Operations With Functions

[2.4.2.30] *Dynamic Item*

30. At a picture frame shop you order a $44 picture frame. You have a $30 gift certificate and a 15% discount coupon. The picture frame shop allows you to use both discounts at once, and gives you the option of which discount is taken first. Use composition of the following functions to make your decision. In which order should you take the discounts to obtain the lowest price?

$$d(x) = x - 30.00$$
$$p(x) = 0.85x$$

[A] $d(p(x)) = 0.85x - 25.50, \ d(p(44)) = \$11.90$
   $p(d(x)) = 0.85x - 30.00, \ p(d(44)) = \$7.40$
   You should use the $30 gift certificate first.

[B] $d(p(x)) = 0.85x - 30.00, \ d(p(44)) = \$11.90$
   $p(d(x)) = 0.85x - 25.50, \ p(d(44)) = \$7.40$
   You should use the $30 gift certificate first.

[C] $d(p(x)) = 0.85x - 30.00, \ d(p(44)) = \$7.40$
   $p(d(x)) = 0.85x - 25.50, \ p(d(44)) = \$11.90$
   You should use the 15% discount coupon first.

[D] $d(p(x)) = 0.85x - 25.50, \ d(p(44)) = \$7.40$
   $p(d(x)) = 0.85x - 30.00, \ p(d(44)) = \$11.90$
   You should use the 15% discount coupon first.

[2.4.2.31] *Dynamic Item*

31. For the pair of functions, $f$ and $g$, find $(g \circ f)(x)$ and $(f \circ g)(x)$.
   $$f(x) = 2 + x, \ g(x) = x^2 - 1$$

### Lesson 4:  Operations With Functions

[2.4.2.32]  *Dynamic Item*

32.  You are at a very expensive restaurant and want to order a $77 entree. You have a discount coupon for $50 and a coupon for 17% off. This restaurant allows you to use both coupons at once and will give you the option of which discount is taken first. Solve for the compositions of the following functions in both orders, and then evaluate after substituting the price of the entree for $x$ to make your decision. In which order should you take the discounts to obtain the lowest price?

$d(x) = x - 50.00$

$p(x) = 0.83x$

### Lesson 5:  Inverses of Functions

Objective 1:  Find the inverse of a relation or a function.

[2.5.1.33]  *Dynamic Item*

33.  Find the inverse of the function.

$f(x) = \{(-6, \ -3), \ (-3, \ -6), \ (1, \ -4)\}$

[A] $f^{-1}(x) = \{(-3, \ -6), \ (-6, \ -3), \ (-4, \ 1)\}$

[B] $f^{-1}(x) = \{(-3, \ -6), \ (-6, \ -4), \ (-4, \ -4)\}$

[C] $f^{-1}(x) = \{(-3, \ -6), \ (-6, \ 1), \ (-4, \ 1)\}$      [D] none of these

[2.5.1.34]  *Dynamic Item*

34.  Find the inverse of the function.

$f(x) = 3x + 2$

[A] $f^{-1}(x) = 3x - \dfrac{2}{3}$ 　　　　　　　　 [B] $f^{-1}(x) = x + \dfrac{2}{3}$

[C] $f^{-1}(x) = \dfrac{1}{3}x + \dfrac{2}{3}$ 　　　　　　 [D] $f^{-1}(x) = \dfrac{1}{3}x - \dfrac{2}{3}$

**Lesson 5: Inverses of Functions**

[2.5.1.35] *Dynamic Item*

35. Find the inverse of the function.

$f(x) = \{(6, -4), (-4, 6), (-2, 3)\}$

[2.5.1.36] *Dynamic Item*

36. Find the inverse of the function.

$f(x) = \dfrac{x+2}{4}$

Objective 2: Determine whether the inverse of a function is a function.

[2.5.2.37] *Dynamic Item*

37. Graph the function $y = 2x^2 - 4$, and then graph its inverse as a reflection over the line $y = x$. Is the inverse of the graph also a function?

[A]

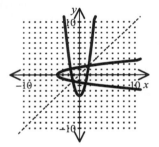

No

[B]

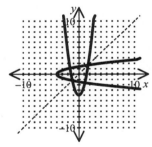

Yes

[C]

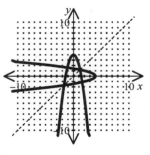

No

[D]

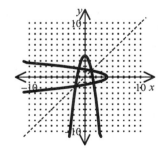

Yes

**Lesson 5: Inverses of Functions**

[2.5.2.38] *Dynamic Item*

38. Find the inverse of the function and determine whether the inverse is a function.
$y = 13x^2$

[A] $y = \pm\sqrt{\dfrac{x}{13}}$, $y$ is a function.

[B] $y = \pm\dfrac{1}{13}\sqrt{x}$, $y$ is not a function.

[C] $y = \pm\sqrt{\dfrac{x}{13}}$, $y$ is not a function.

[D] $y = \pm\dfrac{1}{13}\sqrt{x}$, $y$ is a function.

[2.5.2.39] *Dynamic Item*

39. Find the inverse of the function and determine whether the inverse is a function.
$f(x) = 13x^2$

[2.5.2.40] *Dynamic Item*

40. Graph the function $y = x^2 - 5$, and then use the horizontal-line test to determine whether its inverse is a function.

**Lesson 6: Special Functions**

Objective 1: Write, graph, and apply special functions: piecewise, step, and absolute value.

[2.6.1.41] *Dynamic Item*

41. Graph the function.

$$\begin{cases} y = -x - 1 & \text{if} \quad x < -2 \\ y = 2x + 5 & \text{if} \quad x \geq -2 \end{cases}$$

[A]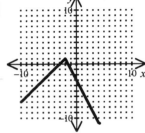

[B]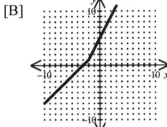

[C]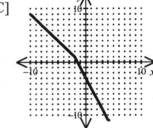

[D]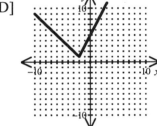

**Lesson 6: Special Functions**

[2.6.1.42] *Dynamic Item*

42. Graph the function.
$f(x) = [5x + 5]$

[A]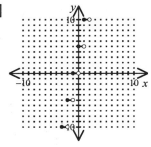

[B]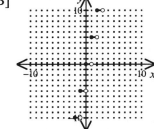

[C]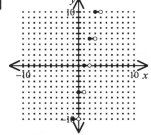

[D]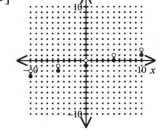

[2.6.1.43] *Dynamic Item*

43. Graph the function.
$y = \dfrac{1}{2}|x|$

**Lesson 6: Special Functions**

[2.6.1.44] *Dynamic Item*

44. Write the equations for the function shown.

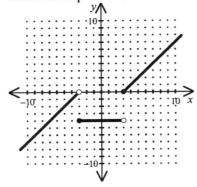

**Lesson 7: A Preview of Transformations**

Objective 1: Identify the transformation(s) from one function to another.

[2.7.1.45] *Dynamic Item*

45. Describe how the graph of the function $y = f(x) - 6$ can be obtained from the graph of $y = f(x)$.

[A] move it up 6      [B] move it 6 to the left

[C] move it down 6     [D] move it 6 to the right

[2.7.1.46] *Dynamic Item*

46. The graph of $f(x) = |x|$ is compressed vertically by a factor of $\frac{1}{5}$, reflected across the $x$-axis, translated 4 units to the left, and translated 8 units downward. Determine the equation of the transformed function, $g(x)$.

[A] $g(x) = 5|x - 4| - 8$      [B] $g(x) = \frac{1}{8}|x + 4| - \frac{1}{5}$

[C] $g(x) = -\frac{1}{5}|x + 4| - 8$     [D] $g(x) = -\frac{1}{5}|x - 4| + 8$

**Lesson 7:  A Preview of Transformations**

[2.7.1.47]  *Dynamic Item*

47.  Describe how the graph of the function $y = \frac{2}{9}(x-8)+0$ can be obtained from the graph of $y = 2(x-1)$.

[2.7.1.48]  *Dynamic Item*

48.  Given the graph of $y = 3(x+2)$, what function would be obtained by moving the graph down 2 and moving it 6 to the right?

**Lesson 1: Operations With Numbers**

Objective 1: Identify and use Properties of Real Numbers.

[2.1.1.1] *Dynamic Item*

[1] [C]

[2.1.1.2] *Dynamic Item*

[2] [B]

[2.1.1.3] *Dynamic Item*

[3] The associative property of multiplication

[2.1.1.4] *Dynamic Item*

    a. associative property of addition
    b. distributive property
    c. commutative property of addition
[4]  d. distributive property

Objective 2: Evaluate expressions using the order of operations.

[2.1.2.5] *Dynamic Item*

[5] [A]

[2.1.2.6] *Dynamic Item*

[6] [C]

[2.1.2.7] *Dynamic Item*

[7] −3

[2.1.2.8] *Dynamic Item*

[8]  36

**Lesson 2:  Properties of Exponents**

Objective 1:  Evaluate expressions involving exponents.

[2.2.1.9] *Dynamic Item*

[9]  [D]

[2.2.1.10] *Dynamic Item*

[10]  [B]

[2.2.1.11] *Dynamic Item*

[11]  −64

[2.2.1.12] *Dynamic Item*

[12]  −1.$

Objective 2:  Simplify expressions involving exponents.

[2.2.2.13] *Dynamic Item*

[13]  [A]

[2.2.2.14] *Dynamic Item*

[14]  [B]

[2.2.2.15] *Dynamic Item*

[15]  $24x^9$

[2.2.2.16]  *Dynamic Item*

[16]  $\dfrac{y^3}{x^9}$

**Lesson 3:  Introduction to Functions**

Objective 1:  State the domain and range of a relation, and tell whether it is a function.

[2.3.1.17]  *Dynamic Item*

[17]  [A]

[2.3.1.18]  *Dynamic Item*

[18]  [B]

[2.3.1.19]  *Dynamic Item*

[19]  No

[2.3.1.20]  *Dynamic Item*

[20]  No

Objective 2:  Write a function in function notation and evaluate it.

[2.3.2.21]  *Dynamic Item*

[21]  [A]

[2.3.2.22]  *Dynamic Item*

[22]  [B]

[2.3.2.23]  *Dynamic Item*

[23]  570,000

[2.3.2.24]  *Dynamic Item*

    a. $C(x) = 6.75x + 26.50$
    b. \$195.25
[24]  c. 35

**Lesson 4:  Operations With Functions**

Objective 1:  Perform operations with functions to write new functions.

[2.4.1.25]  *Dynamic Item*

[25]  [C]

[2.4.1.26]  *Dynamic Item*

[26]  [B]

[2.4.1.27]  *Dynamic Item*

[27]  $(f + g)(x) = -x^2 - x + 6$

[2.4.1.28]  *Dynamic Item*

[28]  $3f(x) - 3g(x) = 3x^2 + 21$

Objective 2:  Find the composition of two functions.

[2.4.2.29]  *Dynamic Item*

[29]  [A]

[2.4.2.30]  *Dynamic Item*

[30]  [C]

[2.4.2.31] *Dynamic Item*

$$(g \circ f)(x) = x^2 + 4x + 3$$

[31] $(f \circ g)(x) = x^2 + 1$

[2.4.2.32] *Dynamic Item*

$$(d \circ p)(x) = 0.83x - 50.00, \ (d \circ p)(77) = \$13.91,$$
$$(p \circ d)(x) = 0.83x - 41.50, \ (p \circ d)(77) = \$22.41$$

[32] You should use the 17% off coupon first.

**Lesson 5: Inverses of Functions**

Objective 1: Find the inverse of a relation or a function.

[2.5.1.33] *Dynamic Item*

[33] [A]

[2.5.1.34] *Dynamic Item*

[34] [D]

[2.5.1.35] *Dynamic Item*

[35] $f^{-1}(x) = \{(-4, \ 6), \ (6, \ -4), \ (3, \ -2)\}$

[2.5.1.36] *Dynamic Item*

[36] $f^{-1}(x) = 4x - 2$

Objective 2: Determine whether the inverse of a function is a function.

[2.5.2.37] *Dynamic Item*

[37] [A]

[2.5.2.38] *Dynamic Item*

[38] [C]

[2.5.2.39] *Dynamic Item*

[39] $f^{-1}(x) = \pm\sqrt{\dfrac{x}{13}}$, $f^{-1}(x)$ is not a function.

[2.5.2.40] *Dynamic Item*

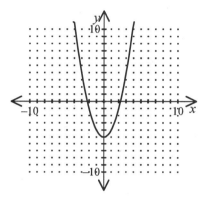

[40] No

**Lesson 6: Special Functions**

Objective 1: Write, graph, and apply special functions: piecewise, step, and absolute value.

[2.6.1.41] *Dynamic Item*

[41] [D]

[2.6.1.42] *Dynamic Item*

[42] [A]

[2.6.1.43] *Dynamic Item*

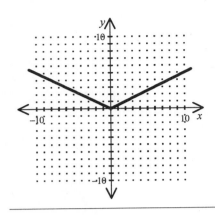

[43] _____

[2.6.1.44] *Dynamic Item*

$$\begin{cases} y = x + 3 & \text{if } -\infty < x < -3 \\ y = -4 & \text{if } -3 \leq x < 3 \\ y = x - 3 & \text{if } 3 \leq x < \infty \end{cases}$$

[44] _____

### Lesson 7: A Preview of Transformations

Objective 1: Identify the transformation(s) from one function to another.

[2.7.1.45] *Dynamic Item*

[45]  [C] _____

[2.7.1.46] *Dynamic Item*

[46]  [C] _____

[2.7.1.47] *Dynamic Item*

[47] vertically compress by a factor of $\frac{1}{9}$, and shift 7 units to the right _____

[2.7.1.48]  *Dynamic Item*

[48]   $f(x) = 3(x-4) - 2$

**Lesson 1: Solving Systems by Graphing or Substitution**

Objective 1: Solve a system of linear equations in two variables by graphing.

[3.1.1.1] *Dynamic Item*

1. Graph and classify the system of equations as *independent*, *inconsistent*, or *dependent*. If the system is independent, find the solution from the graph.
$$\begin{cases} x + y = -3 \\ y = -x - 3 \end{cases}$$

[A]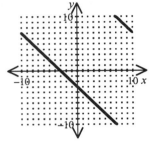

Inconsistent; no solution

[B]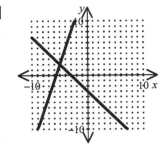

Independent; $(-5,\ 2)$

[C]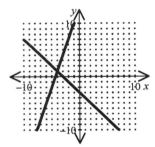

Independent; $(-4,\ 1)$

[D]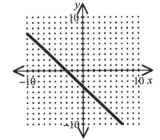

Dependent; infinitely many solutions

[3.1.1.2] *Dynamic Item*

2. Use a graph to solve the system of equations.
$$\begin{cases} x + y = -3 \\ y = 2x - 9 \end{cases}$$

[A] $(-1, -2)$      [B] $(2, -5)$      [C] $(3, -3)$      [D] $(-6, 3)$

**Lesson 1: Solving Systems by Graphing or Substitution**

[3.1.1.3] *Dynamic Item*

3. Use a graph to solve the system of equations.
$$\begin{cases} x + y = 6 \\ y = 3x + 2 \end{cases}$$

[3.1.1.4] *Dynamic Item*

4. Graph and classify the system of equations as *independent*, *inconsistent*, or *dependent*. If the system is independent, find the solution from the graph.
$$\begin{cases} x + 2y = -1 \\ 3x + 6y = -3 \end{cases}$$

Objective 2: Solve a system of linear equations by substitution.

[3.1.2.5] *Dynamic Item*

5. Solve the system of equations by substitution.
$$\begin{cases} 3x + 4y = -26 \\ 3x + y = -11 \end{cases}$$

[A] $(-1, -14)$     [B] $(-2, -5)$     [C] $\left(-5, -2\frac{3}{4}\right)$     [D] $\left(-1\frac{4}{5}, -2\right)$

[3.1.2.6] *Dynamic Item*

6. Solve the system of equations by substitution.
$$\begin{cases} 3y = 3 \\ x + y + z = 7 \\ y + 2z = 5 \end{cases}$$

[A] $(5, 3, -2)$     [B] $(2, 4, 1)$     [C] $(1, 2, 4)$     [D] $(4, 1, 2)$

**Lesson 1: Solving Systems by Graphing or Substitution**

[3.1.2.7]  *Dynamic Item*

7.  Solve the system of equations by substitution.
$$\begin{cases} -3x + y = 11 \\ 8x - 4y = -24 \end{cases}$$

[3.1.2.8]  *Dynamic Item*

8.  Solve the system of equations by substitution.
$$\begin{cases} 3y = 12 \\ x + 4y + 4z = 29 \\ y - 2z = -2 \end{cases}$$

**Lesson 2: Solving Systems by Elimination**

Objective 1: Solve a system of two linear equations in two variables by elimination.

[3.2.1.9]  *Dynamic Item*

9.  Use elimination to solve the system of equations.
$$\begin{cases} 2x + 2y = 18 \\ x - 2y = -6 \end{cases}$$

   [A] $(26, 5)$         [B] $(5, 4)$         [C] $(4, 5)$         [D] $(0, 9)$

[3.2.1.10]  *Dynamic Item*

10.  Use elimination to solve the system of equations.
$$\begin{cases} 4x + 3y = 7 \\ 5x + 4y = -4 \end{cases}$$

   [A] $(4, 3)$     [B] $(40, -51)$     [C] infinitely many     [D] no solution

**Lesson 2:  Solving Systems by Elimination**

[3.2.1.11]  *Dynamic Item*

11.  Use elimination to solve the system of equations.
$$\begin{cases} 3x - y = 22 \\ 8x + 3y = 53 \end{cases}$$

[3.2.1.12]  *Dynamic Item*

12.  Use elimination to solve the system of equations.
$$\begin{cases} 5x - 6y = -39 \\ 7x - 9y = -57 \end{cases}$$

**Lesson 3:  Linear Inequalities in Two Variables**

Objective 1:  Solve and graph a linear inequality in two variables.

[3.3.1.13]  *Dynamic Item*

13.  Graph the linear inequality.
$$5x - 3y < -15$$

[A]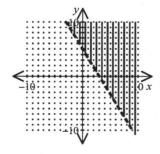

[B]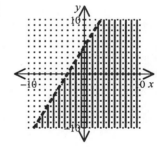

[C]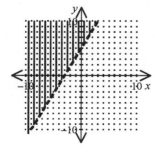

[D]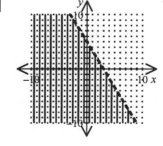

**Lesson 3: Linear Inequalities in Two Variables**

[3.3.1.14]  *Dynamic Item*

14.  Graph the linear inequality.
$4x - 3y \geq -12$

[A]
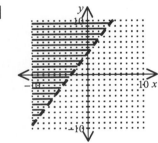

[B]
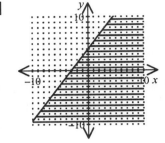

[C]
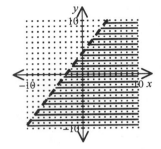

[D]
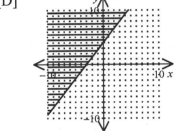

[3.3.1.15]  *Dynamic Item*

15.  Graph the linear inequality.
$-2y > -14$

**Lesson 3: Linear Inequalities in Two Variables**

[3.3.1.16]  *Dynamic Item*

16.  Write an inequality with *y* related to *x* for the graph.

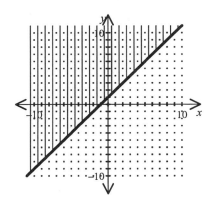

Objective 2:  Use a linear inequality in two variables to solve real-world problems.

[3.3.2.17]  *Dynamic Item*

17.  Which inequality has (4, –4) as a solution?

[A]  $-2x + 2y \leq -20$     [B]  $-x - 2y \geq 8$     [C]  $2x - y \leq 16$     [D]  none of these

[3.3.2.18]  *Dynamic Item*

18.  Determine which ordered pair $(x, y)$ is a solution of $4x - y \leq 9$.

[A]  $(4, 2)$          [B]  $(2, 4)$          [C]  $(2, -12)$          [D]  $(3, -8)$

[3.3.2.19]  *Dynamic Item*

19.  Which of the given ordered pairs are not solutions to the system of inequalities?
$$\begin{cases} 3x + 2y \leq 1 \\ 2x - 3y \geq 1 \end{cases}$$
(1, 3), (–3, 4), (3, –4), (–1, –2), (5, 2)

**Lesson 3: Linear Inequalities in Two Variables**

[3.3.2.20] *Dynamic Item*

20. Determine whether $(-1, -2)$ is a solution of $4x + y \leq -8$. Explain.

**Lesson 4: Systems of Linear Inequalities**

Objective 1: Write and graph a system of linear inequalities in two variables.

[3.4.1.21] *Dynamic Item*

21. Graph the system of linear inequalities.
$$\begin{cases} y \geq -9 \\ y < -5 \end{cases}$$

[A]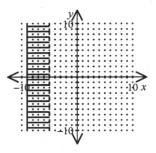

[B]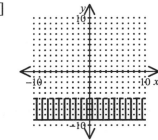

[C]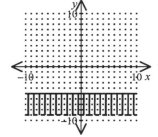

[D]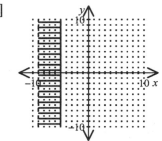

**Lesson 4: Systems of Linear Inequalities**

[3.4.1.22] *Dynamic Item*

22. Graph the system of linear inequalities.

$$\begin{cases} x \geq 0 \\ y \geq 0 \\ x \leq 7 \\ x + y \leq 8 \\ x + 2y \geq 6 \end{cases}$$

[A]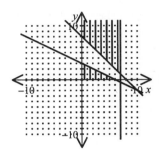

[B]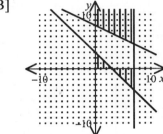

[C]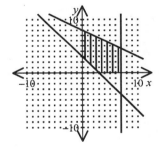

[D]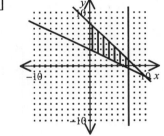

[3.4.1.23] *Dynamic Item*

23. Graph the system of linear inequalities.

$$\begin{cases} y \geq 2x - 5 \\ y \leq -x - 4 \end{cases}$$

**Lesson 4: Systems of Linear Inequalities**

[3.4.1.24] **Dynamic Item***

24. Graph the system of linear inequalities.

$$\begin{cases} x \geq 0 \\ y \geq 0 \\ 5x - 8y \leq 5 \\ 9y \leq 4x + 9 \end{cases}$$

Objective 2: Write a system of linear inequalities in two variables for a given solution region.

[3.4.2.25] *Dynamic Item*

25. Write the system of inequalities whose solution is graphed as the shaded region.

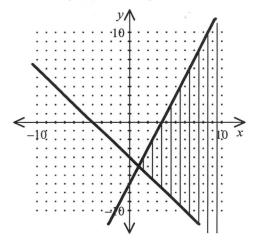

[A] $\begin{cases} y < -4x - 1 \\ y > -x - 7 \end{cases}$   [B] $\begin{cases} y \leq -7x + 2 \\ y \geq -4x - 1 \end{cases}$   [C] $\begin{cases} y \leq 2x - 7 \\ y \geq -x - 4 \end{cases}$   [D] $\begin{cases} y < 2x - 1 \\ y > -x - 7 \end{cases}$

**Lesson 4:** Systems of Linear Inequalities

[3.4.2.26] *Dynamic Item*

26.  Write the system of inequalities whose solution is graphed as the shaded region.

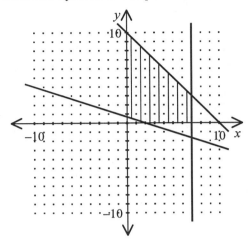

[A] $\begin{cases} x \ge 0 \\ y \ge 0 \\ x \le 7 \\ y \le -x + 10 \\ y \ge -\dfrac{1}{3}x + \dfrac{2}{3} \end{cases}$   [B] $\begin{cases} x \ge 0 \\ y \ge 0 \\ x < 7 \\ y < x + 10 \\ y > -\dfrac{1}{3}x + \dfrac{2}{3} \end{cases}$   [C] $\begin{cases} x \ge 0 \\ y \ge 0 \\ x \le 7 \\ y \le x + 10 \\ y > -\dfrac{1}{3}x + 2 \end{cases}$   [D] $\begin{cases} x \ge 0 \\ y \ge 0 \\ x < 7 \\ y < -x + 10 \\ y \ge -\dfrac{1}{3}x + 2 \end{cases}$

**Lesson 4: Systems of Linear Inequalities**

[3.4.2.27]  *Dynamic Item*

27.  Write the system of inequalities whose solution is graphed as the shaded region.

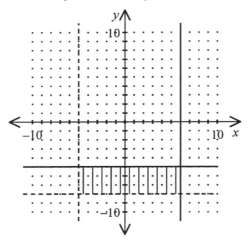

[3.4.2.28]  *Dynamic Item*

28.  Write the system of inequalities whose solution is graphed as the shaded region.

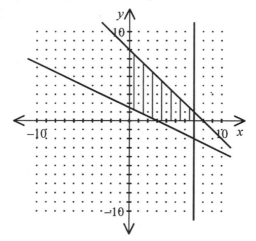

**Lesson 5: Linear Programming**

Objective 1: Write and graph a set of constraints for a linear-programming problem.

[3.5.1.29] *Dynamic Item*

29. Ms. Edwards, an analyst at Multi-Fastener Corp, has developed a model to forecast the company's total production of metal fasteners. Under this model, production, $P$, is equal to 3800 times the man-hours spent producing machine screws plus 3000 times the man-hours spent producing nuts and bolts. Manpower constraints mean that total number of man-hours per year cannot exceed 44,000; logically, the number of man-hours assigned to either task cannot be negative. Express the model in mathematical form.

[A] $P = 3000S + 3800B$
$$\begin{cases} S + B \leq 44{,}000 - (3800 + 3000) \\ S \geq 0 \\ B \geq 0 \end{cases}$$

[B] $P = 3800S + 3000B$
$$\begin{cases} S + B \leq 44{,}000 \\ S \geq 0 \\ B \geq 0 \end{cases}$$

[C] $P = 3000S + 3800B$
$$\begin{cases} S + B \leq 44{,}000 \\ S \geq 0 \\ B \geq 0 \end{cases}$$

[D] $P = 3800S + 3000B$
$$\begin{cases} S + B \leq 44{,}000 - (3800 + 3000) \\ S \geq 0 \\ B \geq 0 \end{cases}$$

**Lesson 5: Linear Programming**

[3.5.1.30] *Dynamic Item*

30. Ms. Reaich, the ticket agent for a small commuter airline, has developed a model to forecast the total monthly revenue from the airline's passenger service. Under this model, the total revenue, $R$, is equal to $358 times the number of first-class, $F$, plus $300 times the number of coach passengers, $C$. Their flight schedule and overall aircraft capacity limit the total number of passengers carried during a single month to a maximum of 30,550. The number of coach class passengers is at least five times the number of first-class passengers, and logically, the number of airline passengers in either class cannot be negative.
Express the model in mathematical form.

[A] $\begin{cases} \$358F + \$300C = R \\ F + C \leq 30{,}550 \\ C \geq 5F \\ F \geq 0;\ C \geq 0 \end{cases}$
　　　　　　　　　　
[B] $\begin{cases} \$358R + \$300F = C \\ C + F \leq 30{,}550 \\ C \geq 5F \\ F \geq 0;\ C \geq 0 \end{cases}$

[C] $\begin{cases} \$358F + \$300C = R \\ F + C \leq 30{,}550 \\ C \leq 5F \\ F \geq 0;\ C \geq 0 \end{cases}$
　　　　　　　　　　
[D] $\begin{cases} \$358R + \$300F = C \\ C + F \leq 30{,}550 \\ C \leq 5F \\ F \geq 0;\ C \geq 0 \end{cases}$

[3.5.1.31] *Dynamic Item*

31. Ms. Kelley, an analyst at MegaCorp, has developed a model to forecast the company's profits from investment. Under this model, profit, $P$, is equal to 0.23 times the investment in equipment plus 0.41 times the investment in labor. Budget constraints mean that total investment in labor and equipment cannot exceed $140,000; logically, investment in labor and equipment cannot be negative. Write and graph the objective function for profit, $P$, and the set of constraints to which it applies.

## Lesson 5:  Linear Programming

[3.5.1.32]  *Dynamic Item*

32. Katrina arranges the transportation for her ski club's ski trips. Skiers can ride one or two charter buses and share a condo for $99, or they can drive themselves and share a condo for $50. The number of skiers who ride the bus, $R$, and the number who drive themslves, $D$, must be less than or equal to 96, the total number of beds available in the condos. There are always enough riders for at least one bus. Each bus can carry up to 40 skiers and must be at least half full to justify chartering the bus, so at least 20 skiers need to ride for one bus and 60 riders for two buses. Logically, the number who drive themselves cannot be negative. Write the objective function for the total cost, C, of the club's ski trip, and the set of constraints to which it applies.

Objective 2:  Use linear programming to find the maximum or minimum value of an objective function.

[3.5.2.33]  *Dynamic Item*

33. Use the set of constraints to find the maximum and minimum values of the objective function $C = 6x + 11y$.
    Constraints:
    $$\begin{cases} x + y \geq 1 \\ 4x - 2y \leq 4 \\ 3y \leq 3x + 3 \end{cases}$$

    [A] The maximum value of $C$ is 73 at $(3, 5)$ and the minimum value is 6 at $(0, 1)$.

    [B] The maximum value of $C$ is 73 at $(3, 5)$ and the minimum value is 6 at $(1, 0)$.

    [C] The maximum value of $C$ is 62 at $(4, 3)$ and the minimum value is 6 at $(0, 1)$.

    [D] The maximum value of $C$ is 62 at $(3, 4)$ and the minimum value is 6 at $(1, 0)$.

**Lesson 5:  Linear Programming**

[3.5.2.34]  *Dynamic Item*

34.  Use the graph of the feasible region for the set of constraints to find the maximum and minimum values of the objective function $C = 2x + 6y$.

Constraints:

$$\begin{cases} x + y \geq 2 \\ 4x - 6y \leq 8 \\ 8y \leq 2x + 16 \end{cases}$$

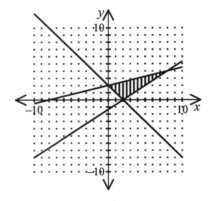

[A]  The maximum value of $C$ is 22 at $(8, 1)$ and the minimum value is 4 at $(0, 2)$.

[B]  The maximum value of $C$ is 22 at $(8, 1)$ and the minimum value is 4 at $(2, 0)$.

[C]  The maximum value of $C$ is 40 at $(8, 4)$ and the minimum value is 4 at $(2, 0)$.

[D]  The maximum value of $C$ is 40 at $(4, 8)$ and the minimum value is 4 at $(0, 2)$.

[3.5.2.35]  *Dynamic Item*

35.  Graph the feasible region for the set of constraints, and find the maximum and minimum values, if they exist, of the objective function $C = 2x + 5y$.

Constraints:

$$\begin{cases} x + y \geq 2 \\ 5x - 2y \leq 10 \\ 4y \leq 3x + 8 \end{cases}$$

### Lesson 5: Linear Programming

[3.5.2.36] *Dynamic Item*

36. Your company manufactures two types of laser printers. The first type, $x$, takes 45 man-hours to manufacture and earns a profit of $93 for each one sold. The second type, $y$, takes 40 man-hours to manufacture and earns a profit of $114 for each one sold. You only have enough parts to build 100 laser printers of either model this month, and a total of 4200 man-hours to work on on them. Model the objective function and the constraints of this situation. Then graph the feasible region, and find the maximum profit and the number of each type of laser printer that will generate the maximum profit. (Remember, unfinished printers *cannot* be sold for a profit.)

### Lesson 6: Parametric Equations

Objective 1: Graph a pair of parametric equations, and use them to model real-world applications.

[3.6.1.37] *Dynamic Item*

37. An airplane, flying at an altitude of 4.98 miles above the ground, has a horizontal speed of 275 miles per hour and is descending at a rate of 22 miles per hour. Use parametric equations to find the airplane's altitude above ground after it has traveled 12 miles, as measured along the ground.

   [A] 7.02 mi          [B] 3.12 mi          [C] 0.40 mi          [D] 4.02 mi

**Lesson 6:  Parametric Equations**

[3.6.1.38]  *Dynamic Item*

38.  Graph the pair of parametric equations for the given restriction on $t$.

$$\begin{cases} x = -3 + 5t \\ y = -4 - 2t \end{cases} \text{ for } t \le 1$$

[A]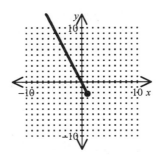

[B]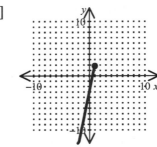

[C]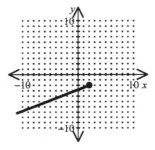

[D]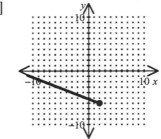

[3.6.1.39]  *Dynamic Item*

39.  Graph the pair of parametric equations for the given restriction on $t$.

$$\begin{cases} x = 1 + 4t \\ y = 5 - t \end{cases} \text{ for } -1 \le t \le 2$$

**Lesson 6: Parametric Equations**

[3.6.1.40] *Dynamic Item*

40. During a tennis game, Venus hits the ball at a height of 3 feet above the ground, with a horizontal velocity of 65 feet per second and a vertical velocity of 7 feet per second. If she is 43 feet away from the net when she hits the ball, use the following parametric equations to answer the three questions:
$$\begin{cases} x(t) = 65t \\ y(t) = 3 + 7t - 16t^2 \end{cases}$$
a. How high will the ball be when it reaches the 3-foot high net? Will it "clear" the net?
b. How far beyond the net will it travel before it hits the ground?
c. Will it land in front of the far court's 39-foot baseline?

Objective 2: Write the function represented by a pair of parametric equations.

[3.6.2.41] *Dynamic Item*

41. Write the pair of parametric equations as a single equation in $x$ and $y$.
$$\begin{cases} x = -6t + 4 \\ y = -5t - 2 \end{cases}$$

[A] $y = \dfrac{5}{3}x - 3$     [B] $y = -\dfrac{5}{6}x + \dfrac{16}{3}$     [C] $y = \dfrac{5}{6}x - \dfrac{16}{3}$     [D] $y = \dfrac{12}{5}x + \dfrac{3}{16}$

[3.6.2.42] *Dynamic Item*

42. Write the pair of parametric equations as a single equation in $x$ and $y$.
$$\begin{cases} x = 2t - 6 \\ y = 4t^2 - 7 \end{cases}$$

[A] $y = 4\left(\dfrac{x+6}{2}\right)^2 - 7$        [B] $x = 2\left(\dfrac{y+7}{4}\right)^2 + 6$

[C] $y = 4\left(\dfrac{x+6}{2}\right)^2 + 7$        [D] $x = 2\left(\dfrac{y+7}{4}\right)^2 - 6$

**Lesson 6: Parametric Equations**

[3.6.2.43]  *Dynamic Item*

43.  Write the pair of parametric equations as a single equation in $x$ and $y$.

$$\begin{cases} x = -5t + 6 \\ y = -8t \end{cases}$$

[3.6.2.44]  *Dynamic Item*

44.  Write the pair of parametric equations as a single equation in $x$ and $y$.

$$\begin{cases} x = 8t^2 - 7 \\ y = 7t - 2 \end{cases}$$

**Lesson 1:  Solving Systems by Graphing or Substitution**

Objective 1:  Solve a system of linear equations in two variables by graphing.

[3.1.1.1]  *Dynamic Item*

[1]   [D]

[3.1.1.2]  *Dynamic Item*

[2]   [B]

[3.1.1.3]  *Dynamic Item*

[3]   (1, 5)

[3.1.1.4]  *Dynamic Item*

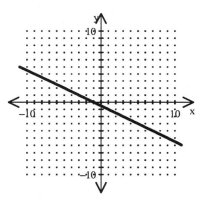

Dependent
[4]   Infinitely many solutions

Objective 2:  Solve a system of linear equations by substitution.

[3.1.2.5]  *Dynamic Item*

[5]   [B]

[3.1.2.6] *Dynamic Item*

[6] [D]

[3.1.2.7] *Dynamic Item*

[7] $(-5, -4)$

[3.1.2.8] *Dynamic Item*

[8] $(1, 4, 3)$

**Lesson 2: Solving Systems by Elimination**

Objective 1: Solve a system of two linear equations in two variables by elimination.

[3.2.1.9] *Dynamic Item*

[9] [C]

[3.2.1.10] *Dynamic Item*

[10] [B]

[3.2.1.11] *Dynamic Item*

[11] $(7, -1)$

[3.2.1.12] *Dynamic Item*

[12] $(-3, 4)$

**Lesson 3: Linear Inequalities in Two Variables**

Objective 1: Solve and graph a linear inequality in two variables.

[3.3.1.13] *Dynamic Item*

[13] [C]

[3.3.1.14]  *Dynamic Item*

[14]  [B]

[3.3.1.15]  *Dynamic Item*

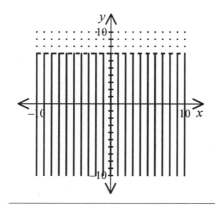

[15]

[3.3.1.16]  *Dynamic Item*

[16]  $y \geq x + 1$

Objective 2:  Use a linear inequality in two variables to solve real-world problems.

[3.3.2.17]  *Dynamic Item*

[17]  [C]

[3.3.2.18]  *Dynamic Item*

[18]  [B]

[3.3.2.19]  *Dynamic Item*

[19]  (1, 3), (5, 2), (–3, 4)

[3.3.2.20]  *Dynamic Item*

[20]  no;  $4 \times (-1) + 1 \times (-2) = -6$, which is $> -8$

**Lesson 4: Systems of Linear Inequalities**

Objective 1: Write and graph a system of linear inequalities in two variables.

[3.4.1.21] *Dynamic Item*

[21]  [B]

[3.4.1.22] *Dynamic Item*

[22]  [D]

[3.4.1.23] *Dynamic Item*

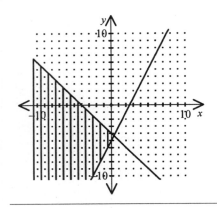

[23]

[3.4.1.24] **Dynamic Item*

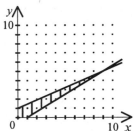

[24]

Objective 2: Write a system of linear inequalities in two variables for a given solution region.

[3.4.2.25] *Dynamic Item*

[25]  [C]

[3.4.2.26] *Dynamic Item*

[26]  [A]

[3.4.2.27] *Dynamic Item*

[27]  $\begin{cases} -8 < y \le -5 \\ -5 < x \le 6 \end{cases}$

[3.4.2.28] *Dynamic Item*

[28]  $\begin{cases} x \ge 0 \\ y \ge 0 \\ x \le 7 \\ y \le -x + 8 \\ y \le -\dfrac{1}{2}x + 1\dfrac{1}{2} \end{cases}$

## Lesson 5:  Linear Programming

Objective 1: Write and graph a set of constraints for a linear-programming problem.

[3.5.1.29] *Dynamic Item*

[29]  [B]

[3.5.1.30] *Dynamic Item*

[30]  [A]

[3.5.1.31]  *Dynamic Item*

$$\begin{cases} P = 0.23E + 0.41L \\ E + L \leq \$140{,}000 \\ L \geq 0 \end{cases}$$

[31] _____

[3.5.1.32]  *Dynamic Item*

[32] $$\begin{cases} \$99R + \$50D = C \\ R + D \leq 96 \\ R \geq 20; \ D \geq 0 \end{cases}$$
_____

Objective 2:  Use linear programming to find the maximum or minimum value of an objective function.

[3.5.2.33]  *Dynamic Item*

[33]  [D]

[3.5.2.34]  *Dynamic Item*

[34]  [C]

[3.5.2.35] *Dynamic Item*

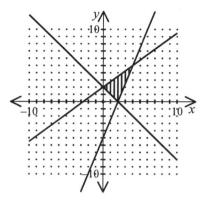

[35] The maximum value of $C$ is 33 at $(4, \ 5)$ and the minimum value is 4 at $(2, \ 0)$.

[3.5.2.36] *Dynamic Item*

$P = \$93x + \$114y$

Constraints:

$$\begin{cases} x + y \leq 100 \\ 45x + 40y \leq 4200 \end{cases}$$

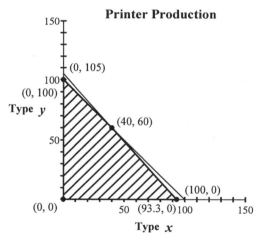

**Printer Production**

[36] $11,400; for 100 of Type $y$.

### Lesson 6:  Parametric Equations

Objective 1:  Graph a pair of parametric equations, and use them to model real-world applications.

[3.6.1.37]  *Dynamic Item*

[37]  [D]

[3.6.1.38]  *Dynamic Item*

[38]  [D]

[3.6.1.39]  *Dynamic Item*

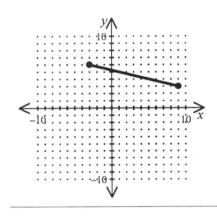

[39]  _____

[3.6.1.40]  *Dynamic Item*

a. 0.6 ft, which does not clear the net
b. not applicable
[40]  c. not applicable  _____

Objective 2:  Write the function represented by a pair of parametric equations.

[3.6.2.41]  *Dynamic Item*

[41]  [C]

[3.6.2.42]  *Dynamic Item*

[42]  [A]

[3.6.2.43]  *Dynamic Item*

[43]  $y = \dfrac{8}{5}x - \dfrac{48}{5}$

[3.6.2.44]  *Dynamic Item*

[44]  $x = 8\left(\dfrac{y+2}{7}\right)^2 - 7$

**Lesson 1:  Using Matrices to Represent Data**

Objective 1:  Represent mathematical and real-world data in a matrix.

[4.1.1.1]  *Dynamic Item*

1.  In May, Bradley bought 28 styrofoam balls and decorated them as toy figurines. In June, he sold 12 figurines. In May, Lupe bought 28 styrofoam balls to decorate and in June, she sold 21 figurines. Which matrix represents all of their May purchases and their June sales?

[A]
$$\begin{array}{c} \text{Bradley} \\ \text{Lupe} \end{array} \begin{array}{cc} \text{May} & \text{June} \\ \begin{bmatrix} 28 & 28 \\ 12 & 21 \end{bmatrix} \end{array}$$

[B]
$$\begin{array}{c} \text{Bradley} \\ \text{Lupe} \end{array} \begin{array}{cc} \text{May} & \text{June} \\ \begin{bmatrix} 28 & -12 \\ 28 & -21 \end{bmatrix} \end{array}$$

[C]
$$\begin{array}{c} \text{Bradley} \\ \text{Lupe} \end{array} \begin{array}{cc} \text{May} & \text{June} \\ \begin{bmatrix} 28 & 16 \\ 28 & 7 \end{bmatrix} \end{array}$$

[D]
$$\begin{array}{c} \text{Bradley} \\ \text{Lupe} \end{array} \begin{array}{cc} \text{May} & \text{June} \\ \begin{bmatrix} 28 & 28 \\ -16 & -7 \end{bmatrix} \end{array}$$

[4.1.1.2]  *Dynamic Item*

2.  Which matrix represents the graph of polygon *MNOP*?

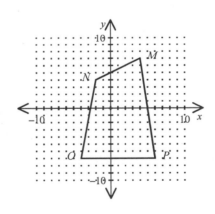

[A]
$$\begin{array}{cccc} M & N & O & P \\ \begin{bmatrix} 4 & 7 & -4 & -7 \\ -2 & 4 & 6 & -7 \end{bmatrix} \end{array}$$

[B]
$$\begin{array}{cccc} M & N & O & P \\ \begin{bmatrix} 4 & -2 & -4 & -7 \\ 7 & 4 & 6 & -7 \end{bmatrix} \end{array}$$

[C]
$$\begin{array}{cccc} M & N & O & P \\ \begin{bmatrix} 7 & 4 & -4 & 6 \\ 4 & -2 & -7 & -7 \end{bmatrix} \end{array}$$

[D]
$$\begin{array}{cccc} M & N & O & P \\ \begin{bmatrix} 4 & -2 & -4 & 6 \\ 7 & 4 & -7 & -7 \end{bmatrix} \end{array}$$

**Lesson 1:  Using Matrices to Represent Data**

[4.1.1.3]  *Dynamic Item*

3.  Gretchen has 37 game cards and 25 baseball cards in her card collection, and Leticia has 61 game cards and 58 baseball cards in her collection. Create and label a matrix to represent both of their collections.

[4.1.1.4]  *Dynamic Item*

4.  Graph the triangle represented by the matrix.

$$\begin{bmatrix} 3 & 5 & 8 \\ 1 & 6 & 5 \end{bmatrix}$$

Objective 2:  Find sums and differences of matrices and the scalar product of a number and a matrix.

[4.1.2.5]  *Dynamic Item*

5.  Perform the indicated operations on the given matrices.

$$\begin{bmatrix} 3 & 1 \\ -4 & -6 \end{bmatrix} + \begin{bmatrix} 5 & 2 \\ -1 & -5 \end{bmatrix}$$

[A] $\begin{bmatrix} -2 & -1 \\ -3 & -1 \end{bmatrix}$   [B] $\begin{bmatrix} 8 & 3 \\ -3 & -1 \end{bmatrix}$   [C] $\begin{bmatrix} -2 & -1 \\ -5 & -11 \end{bmatrix}$   [D] $\begin{bmatrix} 8 & 3 \\ -5 & -11 \end{bmatrix}$

## Lesson 1: Using Matrices to Represent Data

[4.1.2.6]  *Dynamic Item*

6. Perform the indicated operations on the given matrices.

$$\begin{bmatrix} -4 & -7 & -3 \\ 5 & -1 & -6 \\ 0 & 6 & -8 \end{bmatrix} + \begin{bmatrix} -2 & -7 & -9 \\ -4 & 7 & 0 \\ -6 & 3 & 1 \end{bmatrix}$$

[A] $\begin{bmatrix} -6 & -14 & -12 \\ 1 & 6 & -7 \\ -6 & 9 & -6 \end{bmatrix}$ 　　　[B] $\begin{bmatrix} -2 & 0 & 6 \\ 9 & -8 & -9 \\ 6 & 3 & -6 \end{bmatrix}$

[C] $\begin{bmatrix} -6 & -14 & -12 \\ 1 & 6 & -6 \\ -6 & 9 & -7 \end{bmatrix}$ 　　　[D] $\begin{bmatrix} -2 & 0 & 6 \\ 9 & -8 & -6 \\ 6 & 3 & -9 \end{bmatrix}$

[4.1.2.7]  *Dynamic Item*

7. Perform the indicated operations on the given matrices.

$$4 \begin{bmatrix} 4 & 6 & 3 \\ 5 & -8 & -10 \end{bmatrix}$$

[4.1.2.8]  *Dynamic Item*

8. Nicole asked the players on two mens' and women's hockey teams what color their new uniforms should be: red, blue, or green. She recorded the results in two matrices. Find the total for the two teams.

Team 1
$$\begin{array}{c} \\ \text{Men} \\ \text{Women} \end{array} \begin{array}{ccc} R & B & G \\ \begin{bmatrix} 7 & 0 & 6 \\ 1 & 4 & 3 \end{bmatrix} \end{array}$$
　　Team 2
$$\begin{array}{c} \\ \text{Men} \\ \text{Women} \end{array} \begin{array}{ccc} R & B & G \\ \begin{bmatrix} 5 & 1 & 9 \\ 4 & 8 & 0 \end{bmatrix} \end{array}$$

## Lesson 2:  Matrix Multiplication

Objective 1:  Multiply two matrices.

[4.2.1.9]  *Dynamic Item*

9.  Let $A = \begin{bmatrix} 1 & -5 \\ -5 & -5 \end{bmatrix}$, $B = \begin{bmatrix} -1 & -5 \\ 0 & 1 \end{bmatrix}$, and $C = \begin{bmatrix} 1 & 1 \\ 5 & 1 \end{bmatrix}$. Find $AC - CB$.

[A] $\begin{bmatrix} -23 & 0 \\ -25 & 14 \end{bmatrix}$
[B] $\begin{bmatrix} 14 & -25 \\ 0 & -23 \end{bmatrix}$
[C] $\begin{bmatrix} -22 & -1 \\ -25 & 15 \end{bmatrix}$
[D] $\begin{bmatrix} -23 & 14 \\ -25 & 0 \end{bmatrix}$

[4.2.1.10]  *Dynamic Item*

10.  Find $\begin{bmatrix} 2 & 12 & 8 \end{bmatrix} \begin{bmatrix} 5 & 9 \\ 6 & 3 \\ 7 & 6 \end{bmatrix}$.

[A] $\begin{bmatrix} 22 & 144 & 104 \end{bmatrix}$
[B] $\begin{bmatrix} 138 & 102 \end{bmatrix}$
[C] $\begin{bmatrix} 10 & 18 \\ 72 & 36 \\ 56 & 48 \end{bmatrix}$
[D] $\begin{bmatrix} 22 \\ 144 \\ 104 \end{bmatrix}$

[4.2.1.11]  *Dynamic Item*

11.  Let $A = \begin{bmatrix} 1 & -2 \\ -2 & 6 \end{bmatrix}$, $B = \begin{bmatrix} -4 & 6 \\ 0 & 4 \end{bmatrix}$, and $C = \begin{bmatrix} 1 & 1 \\ 2 & 4 \end{bmatrix}$. Find $AC - CB$.

[4.2.1.12]  *Dynamic Item*

12.  Find $\begin{bmatrix} 11 & 16 & 8 \end{bmatrix} \begin{bmatrix} 2 & 17 \\ 13 & 7 \\ 10 & 11 \end{bmatrix}$.

**Lesson 2:  Matrix Multiplication**

Objective 2:  Use matrix multiplication to solve mathematical and real-world problems.

[4.2.2.13]  *Dynamic Item*

13.  The band and the cheerleading squad at a local school are ordering supplies. The supplies they need are listed in the table.

|  | Paint | Paper | Tape |
|---|---|---|---|
| Band | 10 | 13 | 5 |
| Cheerleaders | 10 | 14 | 7 |

If a bottle of paint costs $5, a roll of paper costs $12, and a roll of tape costs $2, which of the following shows the use of matrices to find the total cost of supplies for each group?

[A] $\begin{bmatrix} 10 & 13 & 5 \\ 10 & 14 & 7 \end{bmatrix} \begin{bmatrix} 5 \\ 12 \\ 2 \end{bmatrix} = \begin{bmatrix} 216 \\ 232 \end{bmatrix}$

[B] $\begin{bmatrix} 10 & 13 & 5 \\ 10 & 14 & 7 \end{bmatrix} \begin{bmatrix} 5 \\ 12 \\ 2 \end{bmatrix} = \begin{bmatrix} 448 \end{bmatrix}$

[C] $\begin{bmatrix} 10 & 13 & 5 \\ 10 & 14 & 7 \end{bmatrix} \begin{bmatrix} 5 & 12 & 2 \end{bmatrix} = \begin{bmatrix} 216 \\ 232 \end{bmatrix}$

[D] $\begin{bmatrix} 10 & 13 & 5 \\ 10 & 14 & 7 \end{bmatrix} \begin{bmatrix} 5 & 12 & 2 \end{bmatrix} = \begin{bmatrix} 448 \end{bmatrix}$

**Lesson 2: Matrix Multiplication**

[4.2.2.14] *Dynamic Item*

14. The Student Government secretary, and two teacher's aides are ordering supplies. The supplies they need are listed in the table.

|  | Notebooks | Pens | Paperclips |
|---|---|---|---|
| Secretary | 11 | 9 | 5 |
| Aide No. 1 | 8 | 10 | 4 |
| Aide No. 2 | 8 | 2 | 4 |

If a spiral notebook costs $2.25, a box of pens costs $4.50, and a box of paperclips costs $1.50, which of the following shows the use of matrices to find the total cost of supplies for each person?

[A] $\begin{bmatrix} 11 & 9 & 5 \\ 8 & 10 & 4 \\ 8 & 2 & 4 \end{bmatrix} \begin{bmatrix} \$2.25 & \$4.50 & \$1.50 \end{bmatrix} = \begin{bmatrix} \$158.25 \end{bmatrix}$

[B] $\begin{bmatrix} \$2.25 & \$4.50 & \$1.50 \end{bmatrix} \begin{bmatrix} 11 & 9 & 5 \\ 8 & 10 & 4 \\ 8 & 2 & 4 \end{bmatrix} = \begin{bmatrix} \$65.25 & \$67.50 & \$25.50 \end{bmatrix}$

[C] $\begin{bmatrix} 11 & 9 & 5 \\ 8 & 10 & 4 \\ 8 & 2 & 4 \end{bmatrix} \begin{bmatrix} \$2.25 \\ \$4.50 \\ \$1.50 \end{bmatrix} = \begin{bmatrix} \$72.75 \\ \$69.00 \\ \$33.00 \end{bmatrix}$

[D] $\begin{bmatrix} 11 & 9 & 5 \\ 8 & 10 & 4 \\ 8 & 2 & 4 \end{bmatrix} \begin{bmatrix} \$2.25 \\ \$4.50 \\ \$1.50 \end{bmatrix} = \begin{bmatrix} \$174.75 \end{bmatrix}$

[4.2.2.15] *Dynamic Item*

15. The Art Department and the Homcoming Committee at a local school are ordering supplies. The supplies they need are listed in the table.

|  | Paint | Brushes | Paper | Glue Sticks | Tape |
|---|---|---|---|---|---|
| Art Department | 11 | 14 | 4 | 13 | 6 |
| Homecoming Committee | 10 | 17 | 8 | 16 | 8 |

If a bottle of paint costs $4, a paint brush costs $2, a ream of colored paper costs $8, a box of glue sticks costs $3, and a roll of tape costs $2, use matrices to find the total cost of supplies for each group.

**Lesson 2: Matrix Multiplication**

[4.2.2.16] *Dynamic Item*

16. Mattingly played in 15 basketball games this season, Vitally played in 27 games, and Rivera played in 42 games. Mattingly averaged 6 points and 6 rebounds per game, Vitally averaged 9 points and 13 rebounds, and Rivera averaged 18 points and 13 rebounds. Multiply the following matrices to get the total number of points scored and the total number of rebounds made, by all three players combined.

$$\begin{bmatrix} 15 & 27 & 42 \end{bmatrix} \begin{bmatrix} 6 & 6 \\ 9 & 13 \\ 18 & 13 \end{bmatrix}$$

**Lesson 3: The Inverse of a Matrix**

Objective 1: Find and use the inverse of a matrix, if it exists.

[4.3.1.17] *Dynamic Item*

17. Find the inverse of the following matrix (if it exists): $\begin{bmatrix} -4 & 2 \\ -2 & 5 \end{bmatrix}$

[A] $\begin{bmatrix} 5 & -2 \\ 2 & -4 \end{bmatrix}$ [B] $\begin{bmatrix} -\frac{1}{4} & \frac{1}{8} \\ \frac{1}{8} & \frac{5}{16} \end{bmatrix}$ [C] $\begin{bmatrix} -\frac{5}{16} & \frac{1}{8} \\ -\frac{1}{8} & \frac{1}{4} \end{bmatrix}$ [D] The matrix has no inverse.

**Lesson 3: The Inverse of a Matrix**

[4.3.1.18] *Dynamic Item*

18. Find the inverse of the following matrix (if it exists): $\begin{bmatrix} 2 & -2 & -1 \\ 0 & -1 & 0 \\ -1 & 1 & 1 \end{bmatrix}$

[A] $\begin{bmatrix} 2 & 0 & 1 \\ 0 & -1 & -1 \\ 1 & 0 & 1 \end{bmatrix}$  [B] $\begin{bmatrix} 1 & -1 & 1 \\ 0 & -1 & 0 \\ 1 & 0 & 2 \end{bmatrix}$

[C] $\begin{bmatrix} -1 & 0 & -1 \\ 1 & 1 & 0 \\ -1 & 0 & -2 \end{bmatrix}$  [D] The matrix has no inverse.

[4.3.1.19] *Dynamic Item*

19. Find the inverse of the following matrix (if it exists): $\begin{bmatrix} 3 & 2 & 4 \\ 4 & 3 & 4 \\ 2 & 2 & 1 \end{bmatrix}$

[4.3.1.20] *Dynamic Item*

20. Find the inverse of both $A = \begin{bmatrix} 1 & -4 \\ 2 & 1 \end{bmatrix}$ and $B = \begin{bmatrix} 1 & 4 \\ 3 & -4 \end{bmatrix}$ to determine $A^{-1} - B^{-1}$.

Objective 2: Find and use the determinant of a matrix.

[4.3.2.21] *Dynamic Item*

21. Find the determinant, and tell whether the matrix has an inverse.

$\det \begin{bmatrix} -2 & -2 \\ -7 & -10 \end{bmatrix}$

[A] 6; Yes  [B] −3; Yes  [C] 1; Yes  [D] −1; Yes

**Lesson 3: The Inverse of a Matrix**

[4.3.2.22] *Dynamic Item*

22. Solve: $\det\begin{bmatrix} x-9 & 2 \\ -3 & x-2 \end{bmatrix} = 0$

  [A] $x = 8$      [B] $x = 3$ or $8$      [C] $x = -3$ or $-8$      [D] $x = 3$

[4.3.2.23] *Dynamic Item*

23. Find the determinant, and tell whether the matrix has an inverse.

  $\det\begin{bmatrix} 2 & 6 \\ -4 & 3 \end{bmatrix}$

[4.3.2.24] *Dynamic Item*

24. Solve: $\det\begin{bmatrix} x+2 & 2 \\ 3 & x+7 \end{bmatrix} = 0$

**Lesson 4: Solving Systems With Matrix Equations**

Objective 1: Use matrices to solve systems of linear equations in mathematical and real-world situations.

[4.4.1.25] *Dynamic Item*

25. Write the system of equations as a matrix equation. Then solve the system, if possible, by using a matrix equation. If not possible, classify the system. $\begin{cases} 3x + y = 0 \\ -3x - y = 0 \end{cases}$

  [A] $\begin{bmatrix} 3 & -1 \\ -3 & 1 \end{bmatrix}\begin{bmatrix} x \\ y \end{bmatrix} = \begin{bmatrix} 0 \\ 0 \end{bmatrix}$; inconsistent, no solution

  [B] $\begin{bmatrix} 3 & 1 \\ -3 & -1 \end{bmatrix}\begin{bmatrix} x \\ y \end{bmatrix} = \begin{bmatrix} 0 \\ 0 \end{bmatrix}$; dependent, infinitely many solutions

  [C] $\begin{bmatrix} x & y \end{bmatrix}\begin{bmatrix} 3 & -3 \\ 1 & -1 \end{bmatrix} = \begin{bmatrix} 0 & 0 \end{bmatrix}$; $(6, 2)$      [D] $\begin{bmatrix} 0 \\ 0 \end{bmatrix}\begin{bmatrix} x & y \end{bmatrix} = \begin{bmatrix} 3 & -3 \\ 1 & -1 \end{bmatrix}$; $(6, 6)$

## Lesson 4: Solving Systems With Matrix Equations

[4.4.1.26] *Dynamic Item*

26. Write the system of equations as a matrix equation. Then solve the system, if possible, by using a matrix equation. If not possible, classify the system.
$$\begin{cases} x+2y+3z=-15 \\ x-2y-3z=21 \\ x+2y-3z=9 \end{cases}$$

[A] $\begin{bmatrix} -15 \\ 21 \\ 9 \end{bmatrix} \begin{bmatrix} x & y & z \end{bmatrix} = \begin{bmatrix} 1 & 2 & 3 \\ 1 & -2 & -3 \\ 1 & 2 & -3 \end{bmatrix}$; $(4,\ -3,\ -4)$

[B] $\begin{bmatrix} x & y & z \end{bmatrix} \begin{bmatrix} 1 & 2 & 3 \\ 1 & -2 & -3 \\ 1 & 2 & -3 \end{bmatrix} = \begin{bmatrix} -15 & 21 & 9 \end{bmatrix}$; $(4,\ 3,\ -4)$

[C] $\begin{bmatrix} 1 & 2 & 3 \\ 1 & -2 & -3 \\ 1 & 2 & -3 \end{bmatrix} \begin{bmatrix} x \\ y \\ z \end{bmatrix} = \begin{bmatrix} -15 \\ 21 \\ 9 \end{bmatrix}$; $(3,\ -3,\ -4)$

[D] $\begin{bmatrix} x & y & z \end{bmatrix} \begin{bmatrix} 1 & -2 & 3 \\ -1 & -2 & 3 \\ 1 & -2 & -3 \end{bmatrix} = \begin{bmatrix} -15 & 21 & 9 \end{bmatrix}$; $(3,\ 3,\ 6)$

[4.4.1.27] *Dynamic Item*

27. Write the system of equations as a matrix equation. Then solve the system, if possible, by using a matrix equation. If not possible, classify the system.
$$\begin{cases} 6x-2y=2 \\ 6x-2y=23 \end{cases}$$

[4.4.1.28] *Dynamic Item*

28. Write the system of equations as a matrix equation. Then solve the system, if possible, by using a matrix equation. If not possible, classify the system.
$$\begin{cases} x+3y+z=-11 \\ 2x+7y-4z=-49 \\ x-y-3z=-15 \end{cases}$$

**Lesson 5: Using Matrix Row Operations**

Objective 1: Represent a system of equations as an augmented matrix.

[4.5.1.29] *Dynamic Item*

29. Write the augmented matrix for the system of equations.

$$\begin{cases} -2x+4y=-9 \\ 9x+8y=0 \end{cases}$$

[A] $\begin{bmatrix} -2 & 9 & | & 0 \\ 4 & 8 & | & -9 \end{bmatrix}$    [B] $\begin{bmatrix} -2 & 4 & | & -9 \\ 9 & 8 & | & 0 \end{bmatrix}$    [C] $\begin{bmatrix} -2 & 4 & | & 0 \\ 9 & 8 & | & -9 \end{bmatrix}$    [D] $\begin{bmatrix} -2 & 9 & | & -9 \\ 4 & 8 & | & 0 \end{bmatrix}$

[4.5.1.30] *Dynamic Item*

30. Write the augmented matrix for the system of equations.

$$\begin{cases} 5x-3y-z=0 \\ -3y-6z=1 \\ 3x+3y+2z=1 \end{cases}$$

[A] $\begin{bmatrix} 5 & -3 & -1 & | & 0 \\ 0 & 0 & -6 & | & 1 \\ 0 & 0 & 0 & | & 1 \end{bmatrix}$      [B] $\begin{bmatrix} 5 & -3 & -1 & | & 0 \\ 0 & -3 & -6 & | & 1 \\ 3 & 3 & 2 & | & 1 \end{bmatrix}$

[C] $\begin{bmatrix} 5 & 0 & | & 3 \\ -3 & -3 & | & 3 \\ -1 & -6 & | & 2 \\ 0 & 1 & | & 1 \end{bmatrix}$      [D] $\begin{bmatrix} 5 & -3 & -1 & | & 0 \\ 0 & -3 & 1 & | & -6 \\ 3 & 2 & 3 & | & 1 \end{bmatrix}$

[4.5.1.31] *Dynamic Item*

31. Write the augmented matrix for the system of equations.

$$\begin{cases} -10x+4y=-3 \\ -5x+3y=0 \end{cases}$$

**Lesson 5: Using Matrix Row Operations**

[4.5.1.32] *Dynamic Item*

32. Write the augmented matrix for the system of equations.
$$\begin{cases} 4x + y - 8z = -3 \\ x - 4y - 6z = -1 \\ 6x + 6y + z = -5 \end{cases}$$

Objective 2: Solve a system of linear equations by using elementary row operations.

[4.5.2.33] *Dynamic Item*

33. Which system of equations can be classified as independent?

[A] $\begin{cases} 4x + 7y + 2z = 27 \\ 12x - 6y - 6z = 12 \\ 12x - 6y - 6z = 24 \end{cases}$    [B] $\begin{cases} 6x - 3y - 3z = 6 \\ 18x + 9y - 6z = 69 \\ -6x + 9y - 6z = 21 \end{cases}$

[C] $\begin{cases} -3x - 5y + 4z = -25 \\ -9x - 15y + 12z = -75 \\ 6x + 10y - 8z = 50 \end{cases}$    [D] none of these

[4.5.2.34] *Dynamic Item*

34. Find the reduced row-echelon form of the augmented matrix that represents the following system of equations:
$$\begin{cases} 4x - 10y = 1 \\ -5x + 8y = 0 \end{cases}$$

[A] $\begin{bmatrix} 0 & 1 & \vdots & -\dfrac{4}{9} \\ 1 & 0 & \vdots & -\dfrac{5}{18} \end{bmatrix}$    [B] $\begin{bmatrix} 1 & 0 & \vdots & -\dfrac{1}{160} \\ 0 & 1 & \vdots & \dfrac{1}{250} \end{bmatrix}$    [C] $\begin{bmatrix} 1 & 0 & \vdots & -\dfrac{4}{9} \\ 0 & 1 & \vdots & -\dfrac{5}{18} \end{bmatrix}$    [D] $\begin{bmatrix} 1 & 0 & \vdots & \dfrac{1}{250} \\ 0 & 1 & \vdots & -\dfrac{1}{160} \end{bmatrix}$

## Lesson 5:  Using Matrix Row Operations

[4.5.2.35]  *Dynamic Item*

35.  Classify the following system of equations as inconsistent, dependent, or independent:
$$\begin{cases} -4x - 2y - 5z = -9 \\ -8x + 4y - 10z = 6 \\ 0x - 6y - 15z = -3 \end{cases}$$

[4.5.2.36]  *Dynamic Item*

36.  Solve the system of equations by finding the reduced row-echelon form of the augmented matrix for the following system of equations:
$$\begin{cases} x - 2y + z = 2 \\ 3x - 5y - 3z = 4 \\ 2x - 6y + 15z = -9 \end{cases}$$

**Lesson 1: Using Matrices to Represent Data**

Objective 1: Represent mathematical and real-world data in a matrix.

[4.1.1.1] *Dynamic Item*

[1]  [B]

[4.1.1.2] *Dynamic Item*

[2]  [D]

[4.1.1.3] *Dynamic Item*

$$\begin{array}{c c} & \text{Game} \quad \text{Baseball} \\ & \text{Cards} \quad \text{Cards} \\ \begin{matrix} \text{Gretchen} \\ \text{Leticia} \end{matrix} & \begin{bmatrix} 37 & 25 \\ 61 & 58 \end{bmatrix} \end{array}$$

[3]

[4.1.1.4] *Dynamic Item*

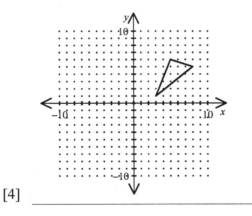

[4]  _____

Objective 2: Find sums and differences of matrices and the scalar product of a number and a matrix.

[4.1.2.5] *Dynamic Item*

[5]  [D]

[4.1.2.6] *Dynamic Item*

[6]  [C]

[4.1.2.7] *Dynamic Item*

[7]  $\begin{bmatrix} 16 & 24 & 12 \\ 20 & -32 & -40 \end{bmatrix}$

[4.1.2.8] *Dynamic Item*

[8]  $\begin{bmatrix} 12 & 1 & 15 \\ 5 & 12 & 3 \end{bmatrix}$

**Lesson 2:  Matrix Multiplication**

Objective 1:  Multiply two matrices.

[4.2.1.9] *Dynamic Item*

[9]  [A]

[4.2.1.10] *Dynamic Item*

[10]  [B]

[4.2.1.11] *Dynamic Item*

[11]  $\begin{bmatrix} 1 & -17 \\ 18 & -6 \end{bmatrix}$

[4.2.1.12] *Dynamic Item*

[12]  $\begin{bmatrix} 310 & 387 \end{bmatrix}$

Objective 2:  Use matrix multiplication to solve mathematical and real-world problems.

[4.2.2.13]  *Dynamic Item*

[13]  [A]

[4.2.2.14]  *Dynamic Item*

[14]  [C]

[4.2.2.15]  *Dynamic Item*

$$\begin{bmatrix} 11 & 14 & 4 & 13 & 6 \\ 10 & 17 & 8 & 16 & 8 \end{bmatrix} \begin{bmatrix} \$4 \\ \$2 \\ \$8 \\ \$3 \\ \$2 \end{bmatrix} = \begin{bmatrix} \$155 \\ \$202 \end{bmatrix}$$

[15]

[4.2.2.16]  *Dynamic Item*

[16]  1089 points, 987 rebounds

**Lesson 3:  The Inverse of a Matrix**

Objective 1:  Find and use the inverse of a matrix, if it exists.

[4.3.1.17]  *Dynamic Item*

[17]  [C]

[4.3.1.18]  *Dynamic Item*

[18]  [B]

[4.3.1.19]  *Dynamic Item*

[19] $\begin{bmatrix} -5 & 6 & -4 \\ 4 & -5 & 4 \\ 2 & -2 & 1 \end{bmatrix}$

[4.3.1.20]  *Dynamic Item*

[20] $\begin{bmatrix} -\dfrac{5}{36} & \dfrac{7}{36} \\ -\dfrac{59}{144} & \dfrac{25}{144} \end{bmatrix}$

Objective 2:  Find and use the determinant of a matrix.

[4.3.2.21]  *Dynamic Item*

[21]  [A]

[4.3.2.22]  *Dynamic Item*

[22]  [B]

[4.3.2.23]  *Dynamic Item*

[23]  30; Yes

[4.3.2.24]  *Dynamic Item*

[24]  $x = -8$ or $-1$

**Lesson 4:  Solving Systems With Matrix Equations**

Objective 1:  Use matrices to solve systems of linear equations in mathematical and real-world situations.

[4.4.1.25]  *Dynamic Item*

[25]  [B]

[4.4.1.26] *Dynamic Item*

[26] [C]

[4.4.1.27] *Dynamic Item*

[27] inconsistent, no solution

[4.4.1.28] *Dynamic Item*

[28] $x = -6$, $y = -3$, $z = 4$

**Lesson 5: Using Matrix Row Operations**

Objective 1: Represent a system of equations as an augmented matrix.

[4.5.1.29] *Dynamic Item*

[29] [B]

[4.5.1.30] *Dynamic Item*

[30] [B]

[4.5.1.31] *Dynamic Item*

[31] $\begin{bmatrix} -10 & 4 & | & -3 \\ -5 & 3 & | & 0 \end{bmatrix}$

[4.5.1.32] *Dynamic Item*

[32] $\begin{bmatrix} 4 & 1 & -8 & | & -3 \\ 1 & -4 & -6 & | & -1 \\ 6 & 6 & 1 & | & -5 \end{bmatrix}$

Objective 2: Solve a system of linear equations by using elementary row operations.

[4.5.2.33]  *Dynamic Item*

[33]  [B]

[4.5.2.34]  *Dynamic Item*

[34]  [C]

[4.5.2.35]  *Dynamic Item*

[35]  independent

[4.5.2.36]  *Dynamic Item*

$$\begin{bmatrix} 1 & 0 & 0 & | & -189 \\ 0 & 1 & 0 & | & -104 \\ 0 & 0 & 1 & | & -17 \end{bmatrix}$$

[36]  $x = -189,\ y = -104,\ z = -17$

**Lesson 1: Introduction to Quadratic Functions**

Objective 1: Define, identify, and graph quadratic functions.

[5.1.1.1]  *Dynamic Item*

1.  Match the function $f(x) = -2(x + 1)^2$ with its graph and coordinates of its vertex.

[A]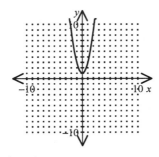

(0, 1)

[B]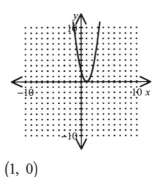

(1, 0)

[C]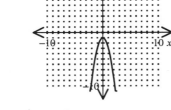

(0, −1)

[D]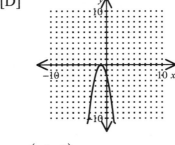

(−1, 0)

[5.1.1.2]  *Dynamic Item*

2.  Which of the following is a quadratic function?

    [A] $f(x) = 7^x + 5$            [B] $f(x) = -2 + 8x^2$

    [C] $f(x) = 6x - 3$            [D] $f(x) = -4x^3 + 9x^2 - 2x - 6$

[5.1.1.3]  *Dynamic Item*

3.  Determine whether the function $f(x) = 4 - 8x$ is a quadratic function. Answer yes or no with an explaination.

Algebra 2
99

**Lesson 1: Introduction to Quadratic Functions**

[5.1.1.4]  *Dynamic Item*

4.  Show that $y - 7 = 7x(-4x + 4) - 5x^2 + 5$ is a quadratic function by writing it in the form $f(x) = ax^2 + bx + c$, and identifying $a$, $b$, and $c$.

Objective 2: Multiply linear binomials to produce a quadratic expression.

[5.1.2.5]  *Dynamic Item*

5.  Show that the function is a quadratic function by writing it in the form $f(x) = ax^2 + bx + c$ and identifying $a$, $b$, and $c$.
    $f(x) = (x + 2)(x + 7)$

    [A] $\begin{aligned} &f(x) = x^2 + 14x + 14 \\ &a = 1,\ b = 14,\ c = 14 \end{aligned}$

    [B] $\begin{aligned} &f(x) = x^2 + 14 \\ &a = 1,\ b = 0,\ c = 14 \end{aligned}$

    [C] $\begin{aligned} &f(x) = x^2 + 14x + 9 \\ &a = 1,\ b = 14,\ c = 9 \end{aligned}$

    [D] $\begin{aligned} &f(x) = x^2 + 9x + 14 \\ &a = 1,\ b = 9,\ c = 14 \end{aligned}$

[5.1.2.6]  *Dynamic Item*

6.  Show that the function is a quadratic function by writing it in the form $f(x) = ax^2 + bx + c$ and identifying $a$, $b$, and $c$.
    $f(x) = (2x - 5)(4x + 9)$

    [A] $\begin{aligned} &f(x) = 8x^2 + 2x - 45 \\ &a = 8,\ b = 2,\ c = -45 \end{aligned}$

    [B] $\begin{aligned} &f(x) = 8x^2 - 2x + 45 \\ &a = 8,\ b = -2,\ c = 45 \end{aligned}$

    [C] $\begin{aligned} &f(x) = 8x^2 + 38x - 45 \\ &a = 8,\ b = 38,\ c = -45 \end{aligned}$

    [D] $\begin{aligned} &f(x) = 8x^2 - 2x - 45 \\ &a = 8,\ b = -2,\ c = -45 \end{aligned}$

[5.1.2.7]  *Dynamic Item*

7.  Show that the function is a quadratic function by writing it in the form $f(x) = ax^2 + bx + c$ and identifying $a$, $b$, and $c$.
    $f(x) = (x + 8)(x + 4)$

## Lesson 1: Introduction to Quadratic Functions

[5.1.2.8]  *Dynamic Item*

8.  Show that the function is a quadratic function by writing it in the form $f(x) = ax^2 + bx + c$ and identifying $a$, $b$, and $c$.

$$f(x) = (5x + 1)(3x + 1)$$

## Lesson 2:  Introduction to Solving Quadratic Equations

Objective 1:  Solve quadratic equations by taking square roots.

[5.2.1.9]  *Dynamic Item*

9.  Solve the equation. Give exact solutions. Then approximate the solution to the nearest hundredth, if necessary.

$$6x^2 = 78$$

[A] $\pm\sqrt{78}$; $\pm 8.83$     [B] $\pm\sqrt{13}$; $\pm 3.61$     [C] $\pm 6\sqrt{13}$; $\pm 21.63$     [D] none of these

[5.2.1.10]  *Dynamic Item*

10.  Solve the equation. Give exact solutions. Then approximate the solution to the nearest hundredth, if necessary.

$$4(x + 2)^2 - 32 = 0$$

[A] $-2 \pm 4\sqrt{8}$; 9.31 or $-13.31$       [B] $2 \pm 2\sqrt{2}$; 4.83 or $-0.83$

[C] $-2 \pm 2\sqrt{2}$; 0.83 or $-4.83$       [D] $-2 \pm 4\sqrt{2}$; 3.66 or $-7.66$

[5.2.1.11]  *Dynamic Item*

11.  Solve the equation. Give exact solutions. Then approximate the solution to the nearest hundredth, if necessary.

$$2x^2 = 26$$

**Lesson 2: Introduction to Solving Quadratic Equations**

[5.2.1.12] *Dynamic Item*

12. Solve the equation. Give exact solutions. Then approximate the solution to the nearest hundredth, if necessary.

$$4(x+4)^2 - 112 = 0$$

Objective 2: Use the Pythagorean Theorem to solve problems involving right triangles.

[5.2.2.13] *Dynamic Item*

13. Find the value of $x$ to the nearest hundredth.

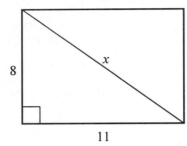

[A] 7.55    [B] 13.6    [C] 13.27    [D] 6.16

[5.2.2.14] *Dynamic Item*

14. What is the missing measure for a right triangle with lengths $b$: 15 inches and $c$: 25 inches; given that $c$ is the length of the hypotenuse?

[A] 400 in.    [B] 850 in.    [C] 20.5 in.    [D] 20 in.

[5.2.2.15] *Dynamic Item*

15. Find the value of $x$ to the nearest hundredth.

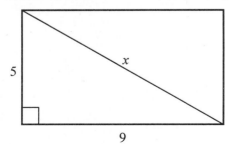

**Lesson 2: Introduction to Solving Quadratic Equations**

[5.2.2.16]  *Dynamic Item*

16. If $c$ is the measure of the hypotenuse of a right triangle, find the missing measure. Round answers to the nearest hundredth. $a = 10$, $b = 6$, $c = ?$

**Lesson 3: Factoring Quadratic Expressions**

Objective 1: Factor a quadratic expression.

[5.3.1.17]  *Dynamic Item*

17. Factor the quadratic expression.
$x^2 + 11x + 28$

   [A] $(x-4)(x-7)$     [B] $(x+4)(x+7)$     [C] $(x+2)(x+14)$     [D] $(x+1)(x+28)$

[5.3.1.18]  *Dynamic Item*

18. Factor the quadratic expression.
$3x^2 - 17x - 28$

   [A] $(x-7)(3x-4)$     [B] $(3x+4)(x+7)$     [C] $(3x-4)(x+7)$     [D] $(3x+4)(x-7)$

[5.3.1.19]  *Dynamic Item*

19. Factor the quadratic expression.
$x^2 - 13x + 42$

[5.3.1.20]  *Dynamic Item*

20. Factor the quadratic expression.
$7x^2 + 20x - 32$

**Lesson 3: Factoring Quadratic Expressions**

Objective 2: Use factoring to solve a quadratic equation and find the zeros of a quadratic function.

[5.3.2.21] *Dynamic Item*

21. Use factoring and the Zero-Product Property to find the zeros of the quadratic function.
$f(x) = x^2 + x - 72$

[A] 1, –72      [B] 36, –2      [C] 18, –4      [D] 8, –9

[5.3.2.22] *Dynamic Item*

22. Use factoring and the Zero-Product Property to solve the quadratic equation $2x^2 + x - 6 = 0$.

[A] $\frac{3}{2}, -2$      [B] 3, –2      [C] 6, –8      [D] $-\frac{3}{2}, 2$

[5.3.2.23] *Dynamic Item*

23. Use factoring and the Zero-Product Property to find the zeros of the quadratic function.
$f(x) = x^2 - x - 30$

[5.3.2.24] *Dynamic Item*

24. Use factoring and the Zero-Product Property to solve the quadratic equation
$3x^2 + 6x - 9 = 0$.

**Lesson 4: Completing the Square**

Objective 1: Use completing the square to solve a quadratic equation.

[5.4.1.25] *Dynamic Item*

25. Solve the equation by completing the square. Give exact solutions.
$x^2 - 2x - 24 = 0$

[A] 4, 6      [B] –4, 6      [C] 4, –6      [D] –4, –6

**Lesson 4: Completing the Square**

[5.4.1.26] *Dynamic Item*

26. Solve the equation by completing the square. Give exact solutions.
    $x^2 + 6x + 1 = 0$

    [A] $\pm 3$        [B] $2 \pm \sqrt{2}$        [C] $2\sqrt{2} \pm 3$        [D] $-3 \pm 2\sqrt{2}$

[5.4.1.27] *Dynamic Item*

27. Solve the equation by completing the square. Give exact solutions.
    $x^2 + 4x - 60 = 0$

[5.4.1.28] *Dynamic Item*

28. Solve the equation by completing the square. Give exact solutions.
    $-9x = 3x^2 - 1$

Objective 2: Use the vertex form of a quadratic function to locate the axis of symmetry of its graph.

[5.4.2.29] *Dynamic Item*

29. Write the quadratic equation in vertex form. Give the coordinates of the vertex and the equation of the axis of symmetry.
    $y = -7x^2 + 42x - 56$

    [A] $y = -7(x + 3)^2 + 7$                      [B] $y = -7(x - 3)^2 - 7$
           $x = -3;\ (-3,\ 7)$                         $x = 3;\ (3,\ -7)$

    [C] $y = -7(x + 3)^2 - 7$                      [D] $y = -7(x - 3)^2 + 7$
           $x = -3;\ (-3,\ -7)$                     $x = 3;\ (3,\ 7)$

**Lesson 4:  Completing the Square**

[5.4.2.30]  *Dynamic Item*

30.  Write the quadratic equation in vertex form. Give the coordinates of the vertex and the equation of the axis of symmetry.

$y = x^2 + 4x - 9$

[A]  $y = (x-2)^2 - 7$
    $(2, 7)$; $x = -2$

[B]  $y = (x-2)^2 - 5$
    $(2, 5)$; $x = -2$

[C]  $y = (x+2)^2 - 5$
    $(-2, -5)$; $x = -2$

[D]  $y = (x+2)^2 - 13$
    $(-2, -13)$; $x = -2$

[5.4.2.31]*Dynamic Item*

31.  Write the quadratic equation in vertex form. Give the coordinates of the vertex and the equation of the axis of symmetry.

$y = x^2 + 6x - 4$

[5.4.2.32]  *Dynamic Item*

32.  Write the quadratic equation in vertex form. Give the coordinates of the vertex and the equation of the axis of symmetry.

$y = \dfrac{4}{3}x^2 - 32x + 201$

**Lesson 5:  The Quadratic Formula**

Objective 1:  Use the quadratic formula to find real roots of quadratic equations.

[5.5.1.33]  *Dynamic Item*

33.  Use the quadratic formula to solve the equation.

$5x^2 - 16x + 3 = 0$

[A]  $-\dfrac{17}{5}, \dfrac{1}{5}$        [B]  $-3, -\dfrac{1}{5}$        [C]  $3, \dfrac{1}{5}$        [D]  $\dfrac{17}{5}, -\dfrac{1}{5}$

**Lesson 5: The Quadratic Formula**

[5.5.1.34] *Dynamic Item*

34. Use the quadratic formula to solve the equation.
$x^2 + 5x + 1 = 0$

[A] $\dfrac{5 \pm \sqrt{21}}{2}$      [B] $\dfrac{-5 \pm \sqrt{29}}{2}$      [C] $\dfrac{-5 \pm \sqrt{21}}{2}$      [D] $\dfrac{5 \pm \sqrt{29}}{2}$

[5.5.1.35] *Dynamic Item*

35. Use the quadratic formula to solve the equation.
$5x^2 + 7x - 6 = 0$

[5.5.1.36] *Dynamic Item*

36. Use the quadratic formula to solve the equation.
$7x^2 - 9x = -1$

Objective 2: Use the roots of a quadratic equation to locate the axis of symmetry of a parabola.

[5.5.2.37] *Dynamic Item*

37. For the quadratic function, write the equation of the axis of symmetry, and find the coordinates of the vertex.
$y = -5x^2 + 20x - 14$

[A] $x = -2;\ (-2,\ -6)$          [B] $x = 2;\ (2,\ 6)$

[C] $x = -2;\ (-2,\ 6)$          [D] $x = 2;\ (2,\ -6)$

[5.5.2.38] *Dynamic Item*

38. For the quadratic function, write the equation of the axis of symmetry, and find the coordinates of the vertex.
$y = x^2 + 6x - 5$

[A] $x = 3;\ (3,\ -4)$          [B] $x = 3;\ (3,\ 31)$

[C] $x = -3;\ (-3,\ 4)$          [D] $x = -3;\ (-3,\ -14)$

**Lesson 5: The Quadratic Formula**

[5.5.2.39] *Dynamic Item*

39. For the quadratic function, write the equation of the axis of symmetry, and find the coordinates of the vertex.

$y = x^2 - 8x - 5$

[5.5.2.40] *Dynamic Item*

40. For the quadratic function, write the equation of the axis of symmetry, and find the coordinates of the vertex.

$y = \dfrac{3}{5}x^2 - 6x + 13$

**Lesson 6: Quadratic Equations and Complex Numbers**

Objective 1: Classify and find all roots of a quadratic equation.

[5.6.1.41] *Dynamic Item*

41. Find the discriminant, and determine the number of real solutions. Then solve.

$x^2 - 2x + 5 = 0$

[A] $-16$; 0; $1 \pm 2i$     [B] $-24$; 0; $-1 \pm 2i$     [C] $-13$; 0; $-1 \pm 4i$     [D] $-6$; 0; $1 \pm 4i$

[5.6.1.42] *Dynamic Item*

42. Find the discriminant, and determine the number of real solutions. Then solve.

$4x^2 + 17x - 15 = 0$

[A] 349; 2; $-\dfrac{3}{4}$, 5    [B] 349; 2; $-\dfrac{3}{4}$, $-5$    [C] 529; 2; $\dfrac{3}{4}$, $-5$    [D] 1036; 2; $\dfrac{3}{4}$, 5

[5.6.1.43] *Dynamic Item*

43. Find the discriminant, and determine the number of real solutions. Then solve.

$4x^2 + 8x + 4 = 0$

**Lesson 6: Quadratic Equations and Complex Numbers**

[5.6.1.44] *Dynamic Item*

44. Find the discriminant, and determine the number of real solutions. Then solve.
$49x^2 - 16 = 0$

Objective 2: Graph and perform operations on complex numbers.

[5.6.2.45] *Dynamic Item*

45. Simplify: $\dfrac{2-3i}{5+i}$

[A] $-\dfrac{7}{26} - \dfrac{17}{26}i$ [B] $\dfrac{7}{26} + \dfrac{17}{26}i$ [C] $\dfrac{7}{26} - \dfrac{17}{26}i$ [D] $-\dfrac{7}{26} + \dfrac{17}{26}i$

[5.6.2.46] *Dynamic Item*

46. Graph the complex number on the complex plane.
$-2 - i$

[A]

Algebra 2
109

**Lesson 6: Quadratic Equations and Complex Numbers**

[B]

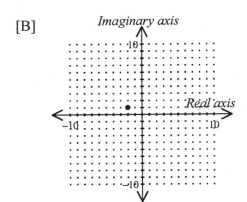

[C]

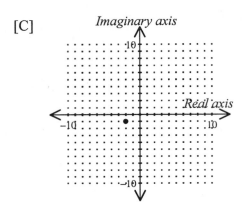

[D]

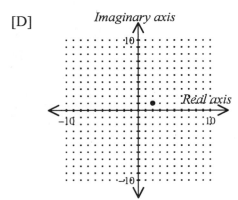

**Lesson 6: Quadratic Equations and Complex Numbers**

[5.6.2.47] *Dynamic Item*

47. Graph the complex number on the complex plane.
$-4 + 4i$

[5.6.2.48] *Dynamic Item*

48. Simplify: $(-2 + 6i)(-3 + 5i)$

**Lesson 7: Curve Fitting With Quadratic Models**

Objective 1: Find a quadratic function that exactly fits three data points.

[5.7.1.49] *Dynamic Item*

49. Find a quadratic function that fits the set of data points exactly, in the form $y = ax^2 + bx + c$ with values of $a$, $b$, and $c$ to two decimal places.
$(2, 4.6), (5, 2.2), (12, 4.3)$

[A] $y = -0.2x^2 + 3.64x - 11.10$      [B] $y = -0.01x^2 - 0.71x + 6.07$

[C] $y = 0.11x^2 - 1.57x + 7.30$      [D] $y = 0.32x^2 - 4.50x + 12.33$

[5.7.1.50] *Dynamic Item*

50. Find a quadratic function that fits the set of data points exactly, in the form $y = ax^2 + bx + c$ with values of $a$, $b$, and $c$ to three decimal places.
$(1, 14.1), (7, 12.8), (11, 14.9)$

[A] $y = -0.063x^2 + 1.650x + 4.312$      [B] $y = -0.171x^2 + 1.150x + 13.121$

[C] $y = 0.074x^2 - 0.810x + 14.836$      [D] $y = 0.308x^2 - 3.610x + 17.403$

**Lesson 7: Curve Fitting With Quadratic Models**

[5.7.1.51] *Dynamic Item*

51. Find a quadratic function that fits the set of data points exactly, in the form $y = ax^2 + bx + c$ with values of $a$, $b$, and $c$ to three decimal places.
$(1, 5.3)$, $(8, 2.3)$, $(12, 5.8)$

[5.7.1.52] *Dynamic Item*

52. Find a quadratic function that fits the set of data points exactly, in the form $y = ax^2 + bx + c$ with values of $a$, $b$, and $c$ to three decimal places.
$(4, 5.4)$, $(6, 2.9)$, $(9, 4.9)$

Objective 2: Find a quadratic model to represent a data set.

[5.7.2.53] *Dynamic Item*

53. Gupta threw a baseball off a cliff into an open field 39 feet below. The chart gives the horizontal distance, $x$ (in feet), the baseball traveled from Gupta and the height, $y$ (in feet), of the baseball above the field.

| distance, $x$ | 11 | 21 | 36 | 46 |
|---|---|---|---|---|
| height, $y$ | 54 | 62 | 64 | 59 |

Choose the quadratic equation that best fits the baseball's trajectory from Gupta to the open field below.

[A] $y = -0.0271(x + 31)^2 + 65$

[B] $y = -0.0371(x + 29)^2 + 65$

[C] $y = -0.0271x^2 + 1.677x + 39$

[D] $y = -0.0371x^2 + 1.545x + 39$

**Lesson 7: Curve Fitting With Quadratic Models**

[5.7.2.54] *Dynamic Item*

54. The turnstiles at the entrance to the State Fair kept track of the number of people entering the fairgrounds, for the first seven hours following the openning of the fair. Find a quadratic equation that models the data shown.

| Time (hr) | 0 | 1 | 2 | 3 | 4 | 5 | 6 |
|---|---|---|---|---|---|---|---|
| People (1000s) | 5.8 | 5.59 | 5.44 | 5.35 | 5.33 | 5.37 | 5.46 |

[A] $0.043x^2 - 0.118x + 4.21$  [B] $0.075x^2 - 0.146x + 7.17$

[C] $0.031x^2 - 0.242x + 5.80$  [D] $0.042x^2 - 0.199x + 4.60$

[5.7.2.55] *Dynamic Item*

55. In an experiment, a petri dish with a colony of bacteria is exposed to cold temperatures and then warmed again. Find a quadratic equation that models the data shown.

| Time (hr) | 0 | 1 | 2 | 3 | 4 | 5 | 6 |
|---|---|---|---|---|---|---|---|
| Population (1000s) | 6.5 | 5.07 | 4.38 | 4.43 | 5.22 | 6.75 | 9.02 |

[5.7.2.56] *Dynamic Item*

56. Steven threw a rock from the top of a steep 55-foot high hill into a pond at the foot of the hill. The chart gives the horizontal distance, $x$ (in feet), the rock traveled from Steven and the height, $y$ (in feet), of the rock above the pond.

| distance, $x$ | 14 | 24 | 41 | 55 |
|---|---|---|---|---|
| height, $y$ | 67 | 71 | 72 | 66 |

Find the quadratic equation that best fits the rock's trajectory from Steven to the pond below.

**Lesson 8:  Solving Quadratic Inequalities**

Objective 1:  Write, solve, and graph a quadratic inequality in one variable.

[5.8.1.57]  *Dynamic Item*

57.  Solve the quadratic inequality, and graph the solution on a number line.
$x^2 - 4x \geq 12$

[A] $x \leq -2$ or $x \geq 6$

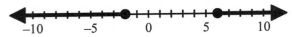

[B] $-6 \leq x \leq 2$

[C] $x \leq -6$ or $x \geq 2$

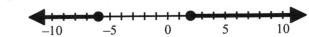

[D] $-2 \leq x \leq 6$

**Lesson 8: Solving Quadratic Inequalities**

[5.8.1.58]  *Dynamic Item*

58.  Solve the quadratic inequality, and graph the solution on a number line.
$x^2 + 3x - 28 < 0$

[A]  $x < -7$  or  $x > 4$

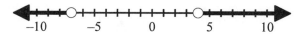

[B]  $x < -4$  or  $x > 7$

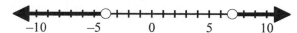

[C]  $-4 < x < 7$

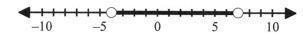

[D]  $-7 < x < 4$

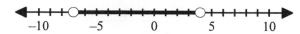

[5.8.1.59]  *Dynamic Item*

59.  Solve the quadratic inequality, and graph the solution on a number line.
$(x + 2)(x - 6) < 0$

[5.8.1.60]  *Dynamic Item*

60.  Solve the quadratic inequality, and graph the solution on a number line.
$x^2 - 4x - 5 < 0$

**Lesson 8: Solving Quadratic Inequalities**

Objective 2: Write, solve, and graph a quadratic inequality in two variables.

[5.8.2.61] *Dynamic Item*

61. Graph the inequality.

$$y \geq -1 - 5x + x^2$$

[A]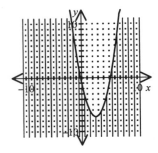

[B]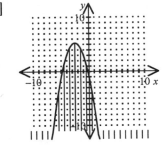

[C]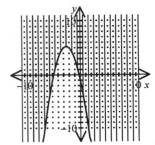

[D]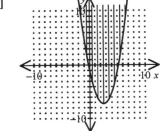

**Lesson 8:  Solving Quadratic Inequalities**

[5.8.2.62]  *Dynamic Item*

62.  Graph the inequality.
$$y > -x^2 + 4x - 3$$

[A]

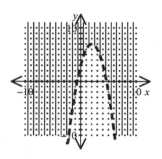

[B]

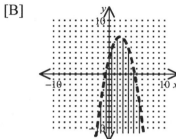

[C]

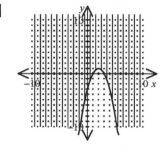

[D]

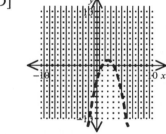

[5.8.2.63]  *Dynamic Item*

63.  Graph the inequality.
$$y > x^2 + 6x + 8$$

[5.8.2.64]  *Dynamic Item*

64.  Graph the inequality.
$$y \leq -x^2 - 5x$$

**Lesson 1: Introduction to Quadratic Functions**

Objective 1: Define, identify, and graph quadratic functions.

[5.1.1.1] *Dynamic Item*

[1] [D]

[5.1.1.2] *Dynamic Item*

[2] [B]

[5.1.1.3] *Dynamic Item*

[3] no; it does not include an $x^2$ term

[5.1.1.4] *Dynamic Item*

$$f(x) = -33x^2 + 28x + 12$$
[4] $a = -33,\ b = 28,\ c = 12$

Objective 2: Multiply linear binomials to produce a quadratic expression.

[5.1.2.5] *Dynamic Item*

[5] [D]

[5.1.2.6] *Dynamic Item*

[6] [D]

[5.1.2.7] *Dynamic Item*

$$f(x) = x^2 + 12x + 32$$
[7] $a = 1,\ b = 12,\ c = 32$

[5.1.2.8] *Dynamic Item*

$$f(x) = 15x^2 + 8x + 1$$

[8] $a = 15, \ b = 8, \ c = 1$

**Lesson 2: Introduction to Solving Quadratic Equations**

Objective 1: Solve quadratic equations by taking square roots.

[5.2.1.9] *Dynamic Item*

[9] [B]

[5.2.1.10] *Dynamic Item*

[10] [C]

[5.2.1.11] *Dynamic Item*

[11] $\pm\sqrt{13}; \ \pm 3.61$

[5.2.1.12] *Dynamic Item*

[12] $-4 \pm 2\sqrt{7}; \ 1.29 \text{ or } -9.29$

Objective 2: Use the Pythagorean Theorem to solve problems involving right triangles.

[5.2.2.13] *Dynamic Item*

[13] [B]

[5.2.2.14] *Dynamic Item*

[14] [D]

[5.2.2.15] *Dynamic Item*

[15] 10.3

[5.2.2.16] *Dynamic Item*

[16]  $\sqrt{136} \approx 11.66$

**Lesson 3:  Factoring Quadratic Expressions**

Objective 1:  Factor a quadratic expression.

[5.3.1.17] *Dynamic Item*

[17]  [B]

[5.3.1.18] *Dynamic Item*

[18]  [D]

[5.3.1.19] *Dynamic Item*

[19]  $(x-6)(x-7)$

[5.3.1.20] *Dynamic Item*

[20]  $(7x-8)(x+4)$

Objective 2:  Use factoring to solve a quadratic equation and find the zeros of a quadratic function.

[5.3.2.21] *Dynamic Item*

[21]  [D]

[5.3.2.22] *Dynamic Item*

[22]  [A]

[5.3.2.23] *Dynamic Item*

[23]  6, −5

[5.3.2.24]  *Dynamic Item*

[24]  −3, 1

**Lesson 4:  Completing the Square**

Objective 1:  Use completing the square to solve a quadratic equation.

[5.4.1.25]  *Dynamic Item*

[25]  [B]

[5.4.1.26]  *Dynamic Item*

[26]  [D]

[5.4.1.27]  *Dynamic Item*

[27]  −10, 6

[5.4.1.28]  *Dynamic Item*

[28]  $\dfrac{-9 \pm \sqrt{93}}{6}$

Objective 2:  Use the vertex form of a quadratic function to locate the axis of symmetry of its graph.

[5.4.2.29]  *Dynamic Item*

[29]  [D]

[5.4.2.30]  *Dynamic Item*

[30]  [D]

[5.4.2.31]*Dynamic Item*

$$y = (x+3)^2 - 13$$

[31] $(-3, -13); x = -3$

[5.4.2.32] *Dynamic Item*

$$y = \frac{4}{3}(x-12)^2 + 9$$

[32] $(12, 9); x = 12$

**Lesson 5:  The Quadratic Formula**

Objective 1:  Use the quadratic formula to find real roots of quadratic equations.

[5.5.1.33] *Dynamic Item*

[33] [C]

[5.5.1.34] *Dynamic Item*

[34] [C]

[5.5.1.35] *Dynamic Item*

[35] $x = -2$ or $x = \dfrac{3}{5}$

[5.5.1.36] *Dynamic Item*

[36] $\dfrac{9 \pm \sqrt{53}}{14}$

Objective 2:  Use the roots of a quadratic equation to locate the axis of symmetry of a parabola.

[5.5.2.37] *Dynamic Item*

[37] [B]

[5.5.2.38] *Dynamic Item*

[38]  [D]

[5.5.2.39] *Dynamic Item*

[39]  $x = 4;\ (4,\ -21)$

[5.5.2.40] *Dynamic Item*

[40]  $x = 5;\ (5,\ -2)$

**Lesson 6:  Quadratic Equations and Complex Numbers**

Objective 1:  Classify and find all roots of a quadratic equation.

[5.6.1.41] *Dynamic Item*

[41]  [A]

[5.6.1.42] *Dynamic Item*

[42]  [C]

[5.6.1.43] *Dynamic Item*

[43]  $0;\ 1;\ -1$

[5.6.1.44] *Dynamic Item*

[44]  $3136;\ 2;\ -\dfrac{4}{7},\ \dfrac{4}{7}$

Objective 2:  Graph and perform operations on complex numbers.

[5.6.2.45] *Dynamic Item*

[45]  [C]

[5.6.2.46]  *Dynamic Item*

[46]   [C]

[5.6.2.47]  *Dynamic Item*

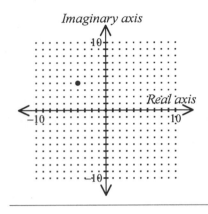

[47]   _____

[5.6.2.48]  *Dynamic Item*

[48]   $-24-28i$   _____

**Lesson 7:  Curve Fitting With Quadratic Models**

Objective 1:  Find a quadratic function that exactly fits three data points.

[5.7.1.49]  *Dynamic Item*

[49]   [C]

[5.7.1.50]  *Dynamic Item*

[50]   [C]

[5.7.1.51]  *Dynamic Item*

[51]   $y = 0.119x^2 - 1.495x + 6.677$   _____

[5.7.1.52]  *Dynamic Item*

[52]  $y = 0.383x^2 - 5.083x + 19.600$

Objective 2:  Find a quadratic model to represent a data set.

[5.7.2.53]  *Dynamic Item*

[53]  [C]

[5.7.2.54]  *Dynamic Item*

[54]  [C]

[5.7.2.55]  *Dynamic Item*

[55]  $0.37x^2 - 1.80x + 6.50$

[5.7.2.56]  *Dynamic Item*

[56]  $y = -0.0156x^2 + 1.059x + 55$

**Lesson 8:  Solving Quadratic Inequalities**

Objective 1:  Write, solve, and graph a quadratic inequality in one variable.

[5.8.1.57]  *Dynamic Item*

[57]  [A]

[5.8.1.58]  *Dynamic Item*

[58]  [D]

[5.8.1.59] *Dynamic Item*

$-2 < x < 6$

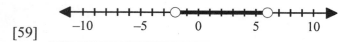

[59]

[5.8.1.60] *Dynamic Item*

$-1 < x < 5$

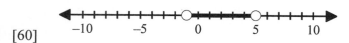

[60]

Objective 2: Write, solve, and graph a quadratic inequality in two variables.

[5.8.2.61] *Dynamic Item*

[61]  [D]

[5.8.2.62] *Dynamic Item*

[62]  [D]

[5.8.2.63] *Dynamic Item*

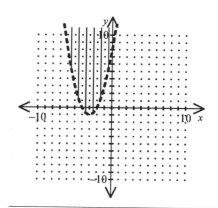

[63]

[5.8.2.64]  *Dynamic Item*

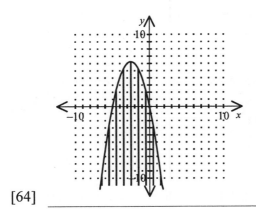

[64] _____

### Lesson 1: Exponential Growth and Decay

Objective 1: Determine the multiplier for exponential growth and decay.

[6.1.1.1] *Dynamic Item*

1. A population of 320 animals decreases at an annual rate of 23%. Find the multiplier for the rate of exponential decay.

    [A] 0.23          [B] 0.77          [C] 1.23          [D] 1.77

[6.1.1.2] *Dynamic Item*

2. Erosion gradually reduces the size of a small Pacific island that has a current area of just 270 acres. If the island's area decreases at an annual rate of 0.04%. Find the multiplier for the rate of exponential decay.

    [A] 0.96          [B] 1.04          [C] 1.0004          [D] 0.9996

[6.1.1.3] *Dynamic Item*

3. You deposit $800 in an account that pays 5% interest compounded yearly. Find the multiplier for the rate of exponential growth.

[6.1.1.4] *Dynamic Item*

4. A town with a current population of 738,150, has a growth rate of 2.3%. Find the multiplier for the rate of exponential growth.

Objective 2: Write and evaluate exponential expressions to model growth and decay situations.

[6.1.2.5] *Dynamic Item*

5. The inflation rate of the U.S. dollar is 3.4 percent. What this means is that every year, prices increase by 3.4 percent. If a pound of vegetables cost $1.17 seven years ago, what does it cost now?

    [A] $1.48          [B] $1.21          [C] $0.92          [D] $7.91

**Lesson 1: Exponential Growth and Decay**

[6.1.2.6] *Dynamic Item*

6. The function $E(t) = 3^6 \cdot 3^t$ approximates the number of nematodes in a certain sample of fresh compost after $t$ days. Find the initial number of nematodes when $t = 0$. How many nematodes are there after $\dfrac{5}{2}$ days?

   [A] $3^6$; 11,364      [B] $3^6$; 22,728      [C] 0; 11,364      [D] 0; 22,728

[6.1.2.7] *Dynamic Item*

7. Evaluate $2(3)^x$ for $x = 2.5$.

[6.1.2.8] *Dynamic Item*

8. A scientist found that the number of bacteria in a culture doubled every hour. If there were 5000 bacteria at 1:00 A.M., how many bacteria were there at 7:00 A.M.?

**Lesson 2: Exponential Functions**

Objective 1: Classify an exponential function as representing exponential growth or exponential decay.

[6.2.1.9] *Dynamic Item*

9. Which function represents exponential decay?

   [A] $y(x) = 5(0.3)^x$      [B] $y(x) = 5(2.4)^x$      [C] $y(x) = 5x - 4$      [D] none of these

## Lesson 2: Exponential Functions

[6.2.1.10]  *Dynamic Item*

10.  Describe the value of $b$ for the function $y(x) = -5(b)^x$ to represent a constant.

   [A]  $b$ has a value of exactly 1

   [B]  $b$ has any value between $-\frac{1}{5}$ and $\frac{1}{5}$

   [C]  $b$ has any value greater than $\frac{1}{5}$ or less than $-\frac{1}{5}$

   [D]  $b$ has a value of exactly $-1$

[6.2.1.11]  *Dynamic Item*

11.  Determine whether the function $y(x) = 5(0.55)^x$ represents exponential growth or exponential decay.

[6.2.1.12]  *Dynamic Item*

12.  Tell wether the function $y(x) = 7\left(\frac{4}{5}\right)^x$ represents exponential growth or decay.

Objective 2:  Calculate the growth of investments under various conditions.

[6.2.2.13]  *Dynamic Item*

13.  If a principal of $900 is invested at an annual interest rate of 5% compounded annually, what is the account balance at the end of 8 years?

   [A]  $1330        [B]  $7560        [C]  $1266        [D]  $1260

[6.2.2.14]  *Dynamic Item*

14.  Find the final amount of the investment.
   $2400 at 6% interest compounded monthly for 3 years.

   [A]  $2858.44        [B]  $2544.00        [C]  $2832.00        [D]  $2872.03

**Lesson 2: Exponential Functions**

[6.2.2.15] *Dynamic Item*

15. Find the final amount of the investment.

   $9000 invested at 7% compounded annually for $5\frac{1}{2}$ years.

[6.2.2.16] *Dynamic Item*

16. If a principal of $650 is invested at an annual interest rate of 4% compounded annually, what is the account balance at the end of 7 years?

**Lesson 3: Logarithmic Functions**

Objective 1: Write equivalent forms for exponential and logarithmic equations.

[6.3.1.17] *Dynamic Item*

17. Write the equation $\log_3 \frac{1}{9} = -2$ in exponential form.

   [A] $3^{-2} = \frac{1}{9}$    [B] $2^3 = -9$    [C] $2^3 = -\frac{1}{9}$    [D] $3^{-2} = 9$

[6.3.1.18] *Dynamic Item*

18. Write the equation in logarithmic form.
   $$2^{-3} = \frac{1}{8}$$

   [A] $\log_2 \frac{1}{8} = -3$    [B] $\log_{-3} \frac{1}{8} = -2$    [C] $\log_2 \frac{1}{8} = 3$    [D] $\log_{-3} \frac{1}{8} = 2$

[6.3.1.19] *Dynamic Item*

19. Write the equation in logarithmic form.
   $$6^{-3} = \frac{1}{216}$$

**Lesson 3: Logarithmic Functions**

[6.3.1.20] *Dynamic Item*

20. Write the equation $\log_3 \frac{1}{9} = -2$ in exponential form.

Objective 2: Use the definitions of exponential and logarithmic functions to solve equations.

[6.3.2.21] *Dynamic Item*

21. Solve the equation for $x$.  [A] –2.53   [B] –2.3   [C] 2.8   [D] –2.1
    $10^x = 0.005$

[6.3.2.22] *Dynamic Item*

22. Solve the equation for $x$.  [A] $\frac{1}{4}$   [B] $-\frac{1}{4}$   [C] 4   [D] 5
    $x = \log_{12} 20{,}736$

[6.3.2.23] *Dynamic Item*

23. Solve the equation for $x$.
    $10^x = 0.014$

[6.3.2.24] *Dynamic Item*

24. Solve the equation for $x$.
    $2 = \log_x 100$

**Lesson 4: Properties of Logarithmic Functions**

Objective 1: Simplify and evaluate expressions involving logarithms.

[6.4.1.25] *Dynamic Item*

25. Evaluate $8^{\log_8 4}$.   [A] 4   [B] 32   [C] 12   [D] 8

**Lesson 4: Properties of Logarithmic Functions**

[6.4.1.26] *Dynamic Item*

26. Write the expression as a single logarithm, and simplify if possible.
$\log_c 3x + 6(\log_c x - \log_c y)$

[A] $\log_c \dfrac{3x^7}{y^6}$     [B] $\log_c \dfrac{9x}{6y}$     [C] $\log_c \dfrac{9x^2}{y}$     [D] $\log_c \dfrac{18x^2}{y}$

[6.4.1.27] *Dynamic Item*

27. Write the expression as a single logarithm, and simplify if possible.
$\log_7 49 + \log_7 2401 - \log_7 343$

[6.4.1.28] *Dynamic Item*

28. Evaluate $\log_6 216$.

Objective 2: Solve equations involving logarithms.

[6.4.2.29] *Dynamic Item*

29. Solve $\log_8 5 + 3\log_8 x = \log_8 6$, for $x$.

[A] 1     [B] $\left(\dfrac{6}{5}\right)^{-3}$     [C] $\left(\dfrac{6}{5}\right)^{\frac{1}{3}}$     [D] $\left(\dfrac{5}{6}\right)^{\frac{1}{3}}$

[6.4.2.30] *Dynamic Item*

30. Solve $\log_3(x+4) - \log_3(x-4) = \log_3 5$ for $x$.     [A] 2   [B] –6   [C] 6   [D] 1

[6.4.2.31] *Dynamic Item*

31. Solve $\log_5 3 - \log_5(x-2) = \log_5 2$, for $x$.

**Lesson 4: Properties of Logarithmic Functions**

[6.4.2.32] *Dynamic Item*

32. Solve $\log_2(x+2) - \log_2(x-2) = \log_2 3$ for $x$.

**Lesson 5: Applications of Common Logarithms**

Objective 1: Define and use the common logarithmic function to solve exponential and logarithmic equations.

[6.5.1.33] *Dynamic Item*

33. Solve the equation. Round your answers to the nearest hundredth.
    $7^x = 21$

   [A] 1.56          [B] 0.64          [C] 1.32          [D] 0.85

[6.5.1.34] *Dynamic Item*

34. Solve the equation. Round your answers to the nearest hundredth.
    $7^{x+3} = 42$

   [A] −1.08          [B] −1.38          [C] −2.15          [D] −2.48

[6.5.1.35] *Dynamic Item*

35. Solve the equation. Round your answers to the nearest hundredth.
    $7.2^x = 16$

[6.5.1.36] *Dynamic Item*

36. Solve the equation. Round your answers to the nearest hundredth.
    $14 + 7.08^x = 17$

## Lesson 5: Applications of Common Logarithms

Objective 2: Evaluate logarithmic expressions by using the change-of-base formula.

[6.5.2.37] *Dynamic Item*

37. Evaluate the logarithmic expression to the nearest thousandth.

$$\log_6 \frac{3}{5}$$

[A] −0.915      [B] −0.085      [C] −3.065      [D] −0.285

[6.5.2.38] *Dynamic Item*

38. Evaluate the logarithmic expression to the nearest thousandth.
$\log_2 155$

[A] 7.276      [B] 10.087      [C] 2.522      [D] 6.046

[6.5.2.39] *Dynamic Item*

39. Evaluate the logarithmic expression to the nearest thousandth.

$$\log_7 \frac{9}{8}$$

[6.5.2.40] *Dynamic Item*

40. Evaluate the logarithmic expression to the nearest thousandth.
$\log_4 191$

## Lesson 6: The Natural Base, *e*

Objective 1: Evaluate natural exponential and natural logarithmic functions.

[6.6.1.41] *Dynamic Item*

41. Evaluate the expression to the nearest thousandth. If the expression is undefined, write *undefined*.
ln 8687

[A] 2.829      [B] 9.07      [C] 3.939      [D] 10.18

**Lesson 6: The Natural Base, *e***

[6.6.1.42] *Dynamic Item*

42. Evaluate the expression to the nearest thousandth. If the expression is undefined, write *undefined*.

$2e^{\frac{1}{5}}$

[A] 3.122        [B] 1.316        [C] 1.087        [D] 2.443

[6.6.1.43] *Dynamic Item*

43. Evaluate the expression to the nearest thousandth. If the expression is undefined, write *undefined*.

$\ln \sqrt{e}$

[6.6.1.44] *Dynamic Item*

44. Evaluate the expression to the nearest thousandth. If the expression is undefined, write *undefined*.

$3e^{\frac{1}{5}}$

Objective 2: Model exponential growth and decay processes.

[6.6.2.45] *Dynamic Item*

45. The half-life of carbon-14 is 5700 years. Find the age to the nearest year of a sample at which 38% of the radioactive nuclei originally present have decayed.

[A] 3931 years      [B] 4381 years      [C] 3831 years      [D] 4931 years

[6.6.2.46] *Dynamic Item*

46. If $7500 is invested at an interest rate of 5%, compounded continuously, determine the balance in the account after 2 years. Use the formula $A = Pe^{rt}$.

[A] $55,417.92      [B] $8713.76      [C] $8288.78      [D] $8268.75

**Lesson 6:  The Natural Base, *e***

[6.6.2.47]  *Dynamic Item*

47.  The half-life of carbon-14 is 5700 years. Find the percentage of the original carbon-14 nuclei that remains in a sample after 2257 years have passed.

[6.6.2.48]  *Dynamic Item*

48.  If $5600 is invested at an interest rate of 9.75%, compounded continuously, determine the balance in the account after 7 years. Use the formula $A = Pe^{rt}$.

**Lesson 7:  Solving Equations and Modeling**

Objective 1:  Solve logarithmic and exponential equations by using algebra and graphs.

[6.7.1.49]  *Dynamic Item*

49.  Solve the equation $3^{3x} = 9^{x+3}$.        [A] 1        [B] $\dfrac{3}{2}$        [C] 8        [D] 6

[6.7.1.50]  *Dynamic Item*

50.  Solve the equation for *x*. Write the exact solution and the approximate solution to the nearest hundredth, when appropriate.
$\ln(9x - 3) = 5$

[A] $\dfrac{e^5 - 3}{9} \approx 16.16$        [B] $\dfrac{e^{-3} + 9}{5} \approx 1.81$        [C] $\dfrac{e^5 + 3}{9} \approx 16.82$        [D] $\dfrac{e^{-3} - 9}{5} \approx -1.79$

[6.7.1.51]  *Dynamic Item*

51.  Solve the equation for *x*. Write the exact solution and the approximate solution to the nearest hundredth, when appropriate.
$125^{8x+9} = 25$

# Chapter 6: Exponential and Logarithmic Functions

**Lesson 7: Solving Equations and Modeling**

[6.7.1.52] *Dynamic Item*

52. Solve the equation for $x$. Write the exact solution and the approximate solution to the nearest hundredth, when appropriate.

    $\ln e^{3x} = 5$

Objective 2: Model and solve real-world problems involving exponential and logarithmic relationships.

[6.7.2.53] *Dynamic Item*

53. The magnitude of an earthquake is found by the equation $M = \dfrac{2}{3}\log\dfrac{E}{10^{11.8}}$, where $M$ is the magnitude and $E$ is the energy released. Find the magnitude of an earthquake that released $10^{24.5}$ ergs of energy.

    [A] 8.2          [B] 12.7          [C] 9.5          [D] 8.5

[6.7.2.54] *Dynamic Item*

54. The formula for estimating the number, $N$, of a certain product sold is $N = 2200 \ln(8t + 4)$, where $t$ is the number of years after the product is introduced. What is the expected number of sales 7 years after the product is introduced? Round to the nearest whole number.

    [A] 8860          [B] 9008          [C] 8872          [D] 32,027

[6.7.2.55] *Dynamic Item*

55. A company with loud machinery needs to cut its sound intensity to 58% of its original level. By how many decibels should the loudness be reduced? Use the formula $L = 10\log\dfrac{I}{I_0}$.

[6.7.2.56] *Dynamic Item*

56. Richter magnitude is given by the formula $R = 0.67\log(0.37E) + 1.46$, in which $R$ is the Richter magnitude and $E$ is the energy, in kilowatt-hours, released by the earthquake. What magnitude corresponds to a release of $1.27 \times 10^8$ kwh of energy?

**Lesson 1: Exponential Growth and Decay**

Objective 1: Determine the multiplier for exponential growth and decay.

[6.1.1.1] *Dynamic Item*

[1] [B]

[6.1.1.2] *Dynamic Item*

[2] [D]

[6.1.1.3] *Dynamic Item*

[3] 1.05

[6.1.1.4] *Dynamic Item*

[4] 1.023

Objective 2: Write and evaluate exponential expressions to model growth and decay situations.

[6.1.2.5] *Dynamic Item*

[5] [A]

[6.1.2.6] *Dynamic Item*

[6] [A]

[6.1.2.7] *Dynamic Item*

[7] 31.2

[6.1.2.8] *Dynamic Item*

[8] 320,000

**Lesson 2: Exponential Functions**

Objective 1: Classify an exponential function as representing exponential growth or exponential decay.

[6.2.1.9] *Dynamic Item*

[9]  [A]

[6.2.1.10] *Dynamic Item*

[10]  [A]

[6.2.1.11] *Dynamic Item*

[11]  exponential decay

[6.2.1.12] *Dynamic Item*

[12]  decay

Objective 2: Calculate the growth of investments under various conditions.

[6.2.2.13] *Dynamic Item*

[13]  [A]

[6.2.2.14] *Dynamic Item*

[14]  [D]

[6.2.2.15] *Dynamic Item*

[15]  $13,057.30

[6.2.2.16] *Dynamic Item*

[16]  $855

**Lesson 3: Logarithmic Functions**

Objective 1: Write equivalent forms for exponential and logarithmic equations.

[6.3.1.17] *Dynamic Item*

[17]   [A]

[6.3.1.18] *Dynamic Item*

[18]   [A]

[6.3.1.19] *Dynamic Item*

[19]   $\log_6 \dfrac{1}{216} = -3$

[6.3.1.20] *Dynamic Item*

[20]   $3^{-2} = \dfrac{1}{9}$

Objective 2: Use the definitions of exponential and logarithmic functions to solve equations.

[6.3.2.21] *Dynamic Item*

[21]   [B]

[6.3.2.22] *Dynamic Item*

[22]   [C]

[6.3.2.23] *Dynamic Item*

[23]   −1.85

[6.3.2.24] *Dynamic Item*

[24]   10

Algebra 2

**Lesson 4: Properties of Logarithmic Functions**

Objective 1: Simplify and evaluate expressions involving logarithms.

[6.4.1.25] *Dynamic Item*

[25]  [A]

[6.4.1.26] *Dynamic Item*

[26]  [A]

[6.4.1.27] *Dynamic Item*

[27]  3

[6.4.1.28] *Dynamic Item*

[28]  3

Objective 2: Solve equations involving logarithms.

[6.4.2.29] *Dynamic Item*

[29]  [C]

[6.4.2.30] *Dynamic Item*

[30]  [C]

[6.4.2.31] *Dynamic Item*

[31]  $\dfrac{7}{2}$

[6.4.2.32] *Dynamic Item*

[32]  4

**Lesson 5:  Applications of Common Logarithms**

Objective 1:  Define and use the common logarithmic function to solve exponential and logarithmic equations.

[6.5.1.33]  *Dynamic Item*

[33]  [A]

[6.5.1.34]  *Dynamic Item*

[34]  [A]

[6.5.1.35]  *Dynamic Item*

[35]  1.4

[6.5.1.36]  *Dynamic Item*

[36]  0.56

Objective 2:  Evaluate logarithmic expressions by using the change-of-base formula.

[6.5.2.37]  *Dynamic Item*

[37]  [D]

[6.5.2.38]  *Dynamic Item*

[38]  [A]

[6.5.2.39]  *Dynamic Item*

[39]  0.061

[6.5.2.40]  *Dynamic Item*

[40]  3.789

**Lesson 6: The Natural Base, *e***

Objective 1: Evaluate natural exponential and natural logarithmic functions.

[6.6.1.41] *Dynamic Item*

[41]  [B]

[6.6.1.42] *Dynamic Item*

[42]  [D]

[6.6.1.43] *Dynamic Item*

[43]  $\dfrac{1}{2}$

[6.6.1.44] *Dynamic Item*

[44]  3.664

Objective 2: Model exponential growth and decay processes.

[6.6.2.45] *Dynamic Item*

[45]  [A]

[6.6.2.46] *Dynamic Item*

[46]  [C]

[6.6.2.47] *Dynamic Item*

[47]  76%

[6.6.2.48] *Dynamic Item*

[48]  $11,081.38

**Lesson 7: Solving Equations and Modeling**

Objective 1: Solve logarithmic and exponential equations by using algebra and graphs.

[6.7.1.49] *Dynamic Item*

[49]  [D]

[6.7.1.50] *Dynamic Item*

[50]  [C]

[6.7.1.51] *Dynamic Item*

[51]  $-\dfrac{25}{24}$ ; $-1.04$

[6.7.1.52] *Dynamic Item*

[52]  $\dfrac{5}{3}$

Objective 2: Model and solve real-world problems involving exponential and logarithmic relationships.

[6.7.2.53] *Dynamic Item*

[53]  [D]

[6.7.2.54] *Dynamic Item*

[54]  [B]

[6.7.2.55] *Dynamic Item*

[55]  2.366 decibels

[6.7.2.56]  *Dynamic Item*

[56]   6.6 _____

**Lesson 1: An Introduction to Polynomials**

Objective 1: Identify, evaluate, add, and subtract polynomials.

[7.1.1.1] *Dynamic Item*

1. Evaluate $x^4 - 10x^2 + 24$ when $x = -1$.　　[A] 40　　[B] 8　　[C] 35　　[D] 15

[7.1.1.2] *Dynamic Item*

2. Simplify $7x^2 + 2x - 7 + 8x^2 - x + 3$.

　　[A] $15x^2 + 3x - 4$　　[B] $-x^2 + x - 10$　　[C] $-x^2 + 3x - 10$　　[D] $15x^2 + x - 4$

[7.1.1.3] *Dynamic Item*

3. Evaluate $3x^3 + x^2 + 4$ when $x = -2$.

[7.1.1.4] *Dynamic Item*

4. Simplify $4x^2 + 4x + x^2 + x - 1 + 3$.

Objective 2: Classify polynomials, and describe the shapes of their graphs.

[7.1.2.5] *Dynamic Item*

5. Classify the polynomial by degree and number of terms. Describe the shape of its graph.
　$-x^5 + 3x^3 - x$

　　[A] quintic trinomial; 'W' shaped with 3 turns

　　[B] quartic trinomial; 'W' shaped with 4 turns

　　[C] quintic trinomial; 'W' shaped with 4 turns

　　[D] quartic trinomial; 'W' shaped with 3 turns

## Lesson 1: An Introduction to Polynomials

[7.1.2.6] *Dynamic Item*

6. Classify the polynomial by degree and number of terms. Describe the shape of its graph.
   $x^3 + 2x^2 - 3x + 10$

   [A] quartic binomial; 'S' shaped with 2 turns

   [B] cubic quadrinomial; 'W' shaped with 3 turns

   [C] cubic quadrinomial; 'S' shaped with 2 turns

   [D] quartic binomial; 'W' shaped with 3 turns

[7.1.2.7] *Dynamic Item*

7. Classify the polynomial by degree and number of terms. Describe the shape of its graph.
   $-2x^3 + x$

[7.1.2.8] *Dynamic Item*

8. Classify the polynomial by degree and number of terms. Describe the shape of its graph.
   $4x^3 - 1$

## Lesson 2: Polynomial Functions and Their Graphs

Objective 1: Identify and describe the important features of the graph of a polynomial function.

[7.2.1.9] *Dynamic Item*

9. Determine the end behavior of the graph of the function $f(x) = -2x^4 - 3x^3 + 3x - 1$.

   [A] falls to the left; rises to the right    [B] falls to the left; falls to the right

   [C] rises to the left; falls to the right    [D] rises to the left; rises to the right

**Lesson 2: Polynomial Functions and Their Graphs**

[7.2.1.10]  *Static Item*

10. Graph the function and approximate any local maxima or minima to the nearest tenth. Specify the intervals in which the function is increasing or decreasing.

$$P(x) = -2x^4 - 4x^3 + 5x^2 - 9$$

[A]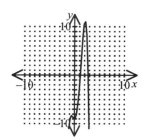

max: $\approx 11.2$ and $\approx -8.3$

min: $\approx -9.0$

increasing: $x < -0.6$, and $0 < x < 2.1$

decreasing: $-0.6 < x < 0$, and $x > 2.1$

[B]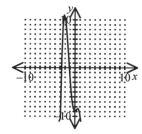

max: $\approx 11.2$ and $\approx -8.3$

min: $\approx -9.0$

increasing: $0 < x < 0.6$, and $x < -2.1$

decreasing: $x > 0.6$, and $-2.1 < x < 0$

[C]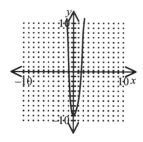

no max

min: $\approx -9.0$

increasing: $x > 0$

decreasing: $x < 0$

[D]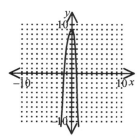

max: $\approx 9.0$

no min

increasing: $x < 0$

decreasing: $x > 0$

**Lesson 2: Polynomial Functions and Their Graphs**

[7.2.1.11] *Static Item*

11. Graph the function and approximate any local maxima or minima to the nearest tenth. Specify the intervals in which the function is increasing or decreasing.
$P(x) = 2x^5 - 2x^4 + 3x^2 - 8x - 3$

[7.2.1.12] *Dynamic Item*

12. Determine the end behavior of the graph of the function $f(x) = -5x^6 - x^4 + 3x^3$.

Objective 2: Use a polynomial function to model real-world data.

[7.2.2.13] *Dynamic Item*

13. The table shows the number of hybrid cottonwood trees planted in tree farms in Oregon since 1987. Find a cubic function to model the data and use it to estimate the number of cottonwoods planted in 1998.

| Years since 1987 | 1 | 3 | 5 | 7 | 9 |
|---|---|---|---|---|---|
| Trees planted (in thousands) | 0.4 | 9.8 | 42.4 | 112.6 | 234.8 |

[A] $T(x) = 0.3x^3 + 0.2x^2 - 0.1$; 423.4 thousand

[B] $T(x) = 0.5x^3 - 0.1x^2 + 0.2$; 418.3 thousand

[C] $T(x) = 0.3x^3 - 0.1x^2 - 0.2x + 0.2$; 423.4 thousand

[D] $T(x) = 0.5x^3 + 0.2x^2 - 0.2x - 0.1$; 418.3 thousand

[7.2.2.14] *Dynamic Item*

14. A biologist took a count of the the number of migrating waterfowl at a particular lake, and recounted the lake's population of waterfowl on each of the next six weeks. Find a quadratic function that models the data shown as a function of $x$, the number of weeks.

| Week | 0 | 1 | 2 | 3 | 4 | 5 | 6 |
|---|---|---|---|---|---|---|---|
| Population | 510 | 303 | 172 | 117 | 138 | 235 | 408 |

[A] $P(x) = 38x^2 - 245x + 510$

[B] $P(x) = 41x^2 - 257x + 504$

[C] $P(x) = 37x^2 - 238x + 504$

[D] $P(x) = 40x^2 - 257x + 510$

### Lesson 2: Polynomial Functions and Their Graphs

[7.2.2.15] *Dynamic Item*

15. The table shows the number of llamas born on llama ranches worldwide since 1988. Find a cubic function to model the data and use it to estimate the number of births in 1999.

| Years since 1988 | 1 | 3 | 5 | 7 | 9 |
|---|---|---|---|---|---|
| Llamas born (in thousands) | 0.3 | 6.7 | 23.5 | 55.5 | 107.5 |

[7.2.2.16] *Dynamic Item*

16. In an experiment, a petri dish with a colony of bacteria is exposed to cold temperatures and then warmed again. Find a quadratic function that models the data shown.

| Time (hr) | 0 | 1 | 2 | 3 | 4 | 5 | 6 |
|---|---|---|---|---|---|---|---|
| Population (1000s) | 6.5 | 5.07 | 4.38 | 4.43 | 5.22 | 6.75 | 9.02 |

### Lesson 3: Products and Factors of Polynomials

Objective 1: Multiply polynomials, and divide one polynomial by another by using long division and synthetic division.

[7.3.1.17] *Dynamic Item*

17. Divide $x^3 + 7x^2 + 15x + 12 \div x + 4$.

[A] $x^2 + 3x + 3$      [B] $x^2 - 3x + 3$      [C] $x^2 - 4x + 3$      [D] $x^2 - 2x - 3$

[7.3.1.18] *Dynamic Item*

18. Write the product as a polynomial in standard form.
$(x+4)(x-4)(x-3)$

[A] $x^3 + 48$                  [B] $x^3 - 7x^2 - 16x + 12$

[C] $x^3 - 3x^2 + 12x - 16$       [D] $x^3 - 3x^2 - 16x + 48$

**Lesson 3:  Products and Factors of Polynomials**

[7.3.1.19]  *Dynamic Item*

19.  Write the product as a polynomial in standard form.
$$(2x^2 - 8x + 2)(x^2 - 9x - 6)$$

[7.3.1.20]  *Dynamic Item*

20.  Divide $(3x^4 - 3x^3 - 6x - 8) \div (x - 2)$ by using long division.

Objective 2:  Use the Remainder and Factor Theorems to solve problems.

[7.3.2.21]  *Dynamic Item*

21.  Use substitution to determine which of the given linear expressions is a *not* a factor of
$3x^4 + 2x^3 - 57x^2 + 52x + 60$.

[A]  $x - 2$　　　　[B]  $x + 5$　　　　[C]  $3x + 2$　　　　[D]  $3x - 2$

[7.3.2.22]  *Dynamic Item*

22.  For the function, use synthetic division and substitution to determine whether the given value is a zero of the function.
$P(x) = 3x^4 - 5x^3 - 59x^2 + 41x + 20$.

[A]  $P(-4)$　　　　[B]  $P(-1)$　　　　[C]  $P(-5)$　　　　[D]  $P(4)$

[7.3.2.23]  *Dynamic Item*

23.  For the function, use synthetic division and substitution to determine whether the given value is a zero of the function.
$P(x) = 3x^4 - 5x^3 - 71x^2 + 157x + 60$, $P(5)$

[7.3.2.24]  *Dynamic Item*

24.  Use substitution to determine whether $3x - 2$ is a factor of $3x^4 - 10x^3 - 17x^2 + 48x + 36$.

**Lesson 4: Solving Polynomial Equations**

Objective 1: Solve polynomial equations.

[7.4.1.25] *Dynamic Item*

25. Use a graph, synthetic division, substitution, and factoring to solve the equation.
$x^3 + 2x^2 - 35x = 0$

[A] 0, 7, 5          [B] 0, –7, –5          [C] 0, 7, –5          [D] 0, –7, 5

[7.4.1.26] *Dynamic Item*

26. Use a graph, synthetic division, substitution, and factoring to solve the equation.
$x^3 + 5x^2 + 2x - 8 = 0$

[A] 2, –2, –4          [B] –1, –2, –4          [C] –2, –2, –4          [D] 1, –2, –4

[7.4.1.27] *Dynamic Item*

27. Use a graph, synthetic division, substitution, and factoring to solve the equation.
$x^3 - x^2 - 14x + 24 = 0$

[7.4.1.28] *Dynamic Item*

28. Use a graph, synthetic division, substitution, and factoring to solve the equation.
$-7x^4 + 63x^2 = 0$

Objective 2: Find the real zeros of polynomial functions and state the multiplicity of each.

[7.4.2.29] *Dynamic Item*

29. Find the real zeros of the function. Give approximate values to the nearest hundredth , if necessary.
$f(x) = x^4 - 7x^3 + 2x^2 + 70x - 120$

[A] 4, 3, $\pm 3.16$          [B] 4, –3, $\pm 3.06$, $\pm -3.16$

[C] –4, 3, $\pm 3.06$          [D] –4, –3, $\pm 3.16$, $\pm -3.06$

**Lesson 4:  Solving Polynomial Equations**

[7.4.2.30]  *Dynamic Item*

30.  Find the real zeros of the function. Give approximate values to the nearest hundredth , if necessary.

$f(x) = x^3 + x^2 + x + 1$

[A] $-1, 0$       [B] 2       [C] 2, 3       [D] $-1$

[7.4.2.31]  *Dynamic Item*

31.  Find the real zeros of the function. Give approximate values to the nearest hundredth , if necessary.

$f(x) = x^4 + x^3 - 23x^2 - 3x + 60$

[7.4.2.32]  *Dynamic Item*

32.  Find the real zeros of the function $f(x) = 6x^4 - 44x^3 + 116x^2 + 116x - 50$. Give approximate values to the nearest hundredth, if necessary.

**Lesson 5:  Zeros of Polynomial Functions**

Objective 1:  Use the Rational Root Theorem and the Complex Conjugate Root Theorem to find the zeros of a polynomial function.

[7.5.1.33]  *Dynamic Item*

33.  Find all the zeros of the polynomial function.

$f(x) = x^3 + x^2 + x + 1$

[A] $0, 2 \pm i\sqrt{2}$       [B] $-1, \pm i$       [C] $-1, 2 \pm \dfrac{i}{2}$       [D] $0, 1 \pm \dfrac{i\sqrt{2}}{2}$

[7.5.1.34]  *Dynamic Item*

34.  Find all the zeros of the polynomial function.

$f(x) = x^2 - 2x + 10$

[A] $-1 \pm 6i$       [B] $1 \pm 6i$       [C] $1 \pm 3i$       [D] $-1 \pm 3i$

**Lesson 5:  Zeros of Polynomial Functions**

[7.5.1.35]  *Dynamic Item*

35.  Find all the zeros of the polynomial function.
$$f(x) = 20x^4 + 265x^3 + 1345x^2 + 1360x + 260$$

[7.5.1.36]  *Dynamic Item*

36.  Find all the zeros of the polynomial function.
$$f(x) = 49x^2 - 25$$

Objective 2:  Use the Fundamental Theorem to write a polynomial function given sufficient information about its zeros.

[7.5.2.37]  *Dynamic Item*

37.  Write a polynomial equation in standard form by using the given information.
     $P$ is of degree 3; $P(0) = 24$; zeros: $-3, 4, 2$

[A] $P(x) = x^3 - 3x^2 - 10x + 24$      [B] $P(x) = x^3 + 3x^2 + 10x + 24$

[C] $P(x) = x^3 + 3x^2 - 10x + 24$      [D] $P(x) = x^3 - 3x^2 + 10x + 24$

[7.5.2.38]  *Dynamic Item*

38.  Write a polynomial equation in standard form by using the given information.
     $P$ is of degree 2; $P(0) = 13$; zeros: $3 + 2i$, $3 - 2i$

[A] $P(x) = x^2 - 5x - 13$      [B] $P(x) = x^2 - 6x + 13$

[C] $P(x) = 2x^2 - 6x - 13$      [D] $P(x) = x^2 + 6x + 13$

[7.5.2.39]  *Dynamic Item*

39.  Write a polynomial equation in standard form by using the given information.
     $P$ is of degree 3; $P(0) = 24$; zeros: $-3, -4, -2$

[7.5.2.40]  *Dynamic Item*

40.  Write an equation that has the given solutions: $3 + 3i$, $3 - 3i$

**Lesson 1: An Introduction to Polynomials**

Objective 1: Identify, evaluate, add, and subtract polynomials.

[7.1.1.1] *Dynamic Item*

[1]  [D]

[7.1.1.2] *Dynamic Item*

[2]  [D]

[7.1.1.3] *Dynamic Item*

[3]  $-16$

[7.1.1.4] *Dynamic Item*

[4]  $5x^2 + 5x + 2$

Objective 2: Classify polynomials, and describe the shapes of their graphs.

[7.1.2.5] *Dynamic Item*

[5]  [C]

[7.1.2.6] *Dynamic Item*

[6]  [C]

[7.1.2.7] *Dynamic Item*

[7]  cubic binomial; 'S' shaped with 2 turns

[7.1.2.8] *Dynamic Item*

[8]  cubic binomial; 'S' shaped with 2 turns

**Lesson 2: Polynomial Functions and Their Graphs**

Objective 1: Identify and describe the important features of the graph of a polynomial function.

[7.2.1.9] *Dynamic Item*

[9]  [B]

[7.2.1.10] *Static Item*

[10]  [B]

[7.2.1.11] *Static Item*

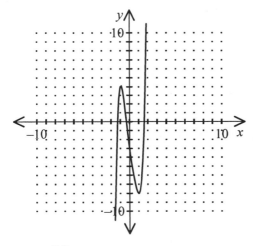

max: $\approx 3.2$

min: $\approx -7.0$

increasing: $x < -0.92$, and $x > 1$

[11]  decreasing: $-0.92 < x < 1$

[7.2.1.12] *Dynamic Item*

[12]  falls to the left; falls to the right

Objective 2: Use a polynomial function to model real-world data.

[7.2.2.13] *Dynamic Item*

[13]  [A]

[7.2.2.14] *Dynamic Item*

[14]  [A]

[7.2.2.15] *Dynamic Item*

[15]  $L(x) = 0.1x^3 + 0.4x^2 + 0.3x - 0.5;\ 184.3$ thousand

[7.2.2.16] *Dynamic Item*

[16]  $P(x) = 0.37x^2 - 1.80x + 6.50$

**Lesson 3:  Products and Factors of Polynomials**

Objective 1:  Multiply polynomials, and divide one polynomial by another by using long division and synthetic division.

[7.3.1.17] *Dynamic Item*

[17]  [A]

[7.3.1.18] *Dynamic Item*

[18]  [D]

[7.3.1.19] *Dynamic Item*

[19]  $2x^4 - 26x^3 + 62x^2 + 30x - 12$

[7.3.1.20] *Dynamic Item*

[20]  $3x^3 + 3x^2 + 6x + 6 + \dfrac{4}{x-2}$

Objective 2: Use the Remainder and Factor Theorems to solve problems.

[7.3.2.21] *Dynamic Item*

[21]  [D]

[7.3.2.22] *Dynamic Item*

[22]  [A]

[7.3.2.23] *Dynamic Item*

[23]  no

[7.3.2.24] *Dynamic Item*

[24]  no

**Lesson 4: Solving Polynomial Equations**

Objective 1: Solve polynomial equations.

[7.4.1.25] *Dynamic Item*

[25]  [D]

[7.4.1.26] *Dynamic Item*

[26]  [D]

[7.4.1.27] *Dynamic Item*

[27]  2, −4, 3

[7.4.1.28] *Dynamic Item*

[28]  0, ±3

Objective 2: Find the real zeros of polynomial functions and state the multiplicity of each.

[7.4.2.29] *Dynamic Item*

[29] [A]

[7.4.2.30] *Dynamic Item*

[30] [D]

[7.4.2.31] *Dynamic Item*

[31] $-5, 4, \pm 1.73$

[7.4.2.32] *Dynamic Item*

[32] $\dfrac{1}{3}, -1$

## Lesson 5: Zeros of Polynomial Functions

Objective 1: Use the Rational Root Theorem and the Complex Conjugate Root Theorem to find the zeros of a polynomial function.

[7.5.1.33] *Dynamic Item*

[33] [B]

[7.5.1.34] *Dynamic Item*

[34] [C]

[7.5.1.35] *Dynamic Item*

[35] $-\dfrac{1}{4}, -1, -6 \pm 4i$

[7.5.1.36] *Dynamic Item*

[36] $\pm \dfrac{5}{7}$

Objective 2: Use the Fundamental Theorem to write a polynomial function given sufficient information about its zeros.

[7.5.2.37] *Dynamic Item*

[37] [A]

[7.5.2.38] *Dynamic Item*

[38] [B]

[7.5.2.39] *Dynamic Item*

[39] $P(x) = x^3 + 9x^2 + 26x + 24$

[7.5.2.40] *Dynamic Item*

[40] $x^2 - 6x + 18 = 0$

## Chapter 8: Rational Functions and Radical Functions

**Lesson 1: Inverse, Joint, and Combined Variation**

Objective 1: Identify inverse, joint, and combined variations, find the constant of variation, and write an equation for the variation.

[8.1.1.1] *Dynamic Item*

1. Use the information to write the appropriate variation equation, and find $y$ for the given values.

   $y$ varies directly as $x$ and inversely as $z$. $y = \dfrac{5}{9}$ when $x = 5$ and $z = 6$. Find $y$ when

   $x = 7$ and $z = 5$.

   [A] $y = \dfrac{2x}{3z}; \dfrac{14}{15}$      [B] $y = \dfrac{2z}{3x}; \dfrac{10}{21}$      [C] $y = \dfrac{3z}{2x}; \dfrac{15}{14}$      [D] $y = \dfrac{3x}{z}; \dfrac{21}{5}$

[8.1.1.2] *Dynamic Item*

2. Use the information to write the appropriate variation equation, and find $y$ for the given values.
   $y$ varies jointly as $x$ and the inverse of $z$. $y = -5$ when $x = -5$ and $z = 6$. Find $y$ when $x = 5$ and $z = -8$.

   [A] $y = \dfrac{z}{3x}; -\dfrac{8}{15}$      [B] $y = \dfrac{6x}{z}; -\dfrac{15}{4}$      [C] $y = \dfrac{xz}{6}; -\dfrac{20}{3}$      [D] $y = \dfrac{6}{xz}; -\dfrac{3}{20}$

[8.1.1.3] *Dynamic Item*

3. Use the information to write the appropriate variation equation, and find $y$ for the given values.

   $y$ varies inversely as $x$. $y = \dfrac{5}{9}$ when $x = 9$. Find $y$ when $x = 8$.

[8.1.1.4] *Dynamic Item*

4. Use the information to write the appropriate variation equation, and find $y$ for the given values.
   $y$ varies jointly as $w$ and $x$ and inversely as $z$. $y = -42$ when $w = 9$, $x = 2$, and $z = -3$.
   Find $y$ when $w = 9$, $x = 3$, and $z = 3$.

**Lesson 1: Inverse, Joint, and Combined Variation**

Objective 2: Solve real-world problems involving inverse, joint, or combined variation.

[8.1.2.5] *Dynamic Item*

5. The Bangor Coat Factory found that the number of coats sold, $N$, varies directly as their advertising budget, $A$, and inversely as the price of each coat, $P$. The Bangor Coat Factory sold 1400 coats when $14,000 was spent on advertising and the price of a coat was set at $70. Determine the number of coats sold when the amount spent on advertising is increased to $70,000.

   [A] 1000          [B] 140          [C] 7000          [D] 7200

[8.1.2.6] *Dynamic Item*

6. The wattage rating of an appliance is given as $W$, in watts, and varies jointly as the resistance, $R$, in ohms, and as the square of the current, $I$, in amperes. If the wattage is 18 watts when the resistance is 50 ohms and the current is 0.6 amperes, find the wattage when the resistance is 100 ohms and the current is 0.3 amperes.

   [A] 30 watts          [B] 60 watts          [C] 9 watts          [D] 3000 watts

[8.1.2.7] *Dynamic Item*

7. A drama club is planning a bus trip to New York City to see a Broadway play. The cost per person for the bus rental varies inversely as the number of people going on the trip. It will cost $14 per person if 79 people go on the trip. How much will it cost per person if 82 people go on the trip?

[8.1.2.8] *Dynamic Item*

8. The amount of oil used by a ship traveling at a uniform speed varies jointly with the distance and the square of the speed. If the ship uses 400 barrels of oil in traveling 400 miles at 36 mph, determine how many barrels of oil are used when the ship travels 360 miles at 18 mph.

Algebra 2
163

### Lesson 2: Rational Functions and Their Graphs

Objective 1: Identify and evaluate rational functions.

[8.2.1.9] *Dynamic Item*

9. Determine whether the function is a rational function. If so, find the domain and identify the horizontal and vertical asymptotes, and any holes in the graph. If the function is not rational, state why not.

$$f(x) = \frac{(9^x - 1)}{(x-9)(x+8)}$$

   [A] rational; $x \neq -9$ or 8; asymptotes at $y = 0$, $x = -9$ and $x = 8$

   [B] rational; $x \neq 1$, 9, or $-8$; asymptotes at $y = 0$, $x = 1$, $x = 9$ and $x = -8$

   [C] rational; $x \neq 9$ or $-8$; asymptotes at $y = 0$, $x = 9$ and $x = -8$

   [D] not rational; $9^x - 1$ is not a polynomial

[8.2.1.10] *Dynamic Item*

10. Determine whether the function is a rational function. If so, find the domain and identify the horizontal and vertical asymptotes, and any holes in the graph. If the function is not rational, state why not.

$$f(x) = \frac{3x - 10}{x^2 + 5x + 4}$$

   [A] rational; $x \neq \dfrac{10}{3}$ or $-1$; asymptotes at $y = 3$, $x = \dfrac{10}{3}$ and $x = -1$

   [B] rational; $x \neq 1$ or 4; asymptotes at $y = 0$, $x = 1$ and $x = 4$

   [C] rational; $x \neq -1$ or $-4$; asymptotes at $y = 0$, $x = -1$ and $x = -4$

   [D] not rational; numerator is of lower degree than denominator

[8.2.1.11] *Dynamic Item*

11. Determine whether the function is a rational function. If so, find the domain and identify the horizontal and vertical asymptotes, and any holes in the graph. If the function is not rational, state why not.

$$f(x) = \frac{2x^2 - 18}{3x^2 - 6x - 9}$$

**Lesson 2: Rational Functions and Their Graphs**

[8.2.1.12] *Dynamic Item*

12. Determine whether the function is a rational function. If so, find the domain and identify the horizontal and vertical asymptotes, and any holes in the graph. If the function is not rational, state why not.

$$f(x) = \frac{6x+6}{7x+4}$$

Objective 2: Graph a rational function, find its domain, write equations for its asymptotes, and identify any holes in its graph.

[8.2.2.13] *Dynamic Item*

13. Which is the graph of the rational function $f(x) = \dfrac{x+4}{x+3}$? Identify the vertical and horizontal asymptotes.

[A]
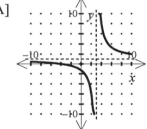
asymptotes: $y = 1$, $x = 3$

[B]
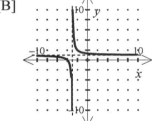
asymptotes: $y = 1$, $x = -3$

[C]
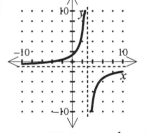
asymptotes: $y = -1$, $x = 3$

[D]
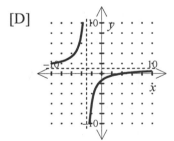
asymptotes: $y = 1$, $x = -3$

**Lesson 2: Rational Functions and Their Graphs**

[8.2.2.14] *Dynamic Item*

14. Which function matches the graph?

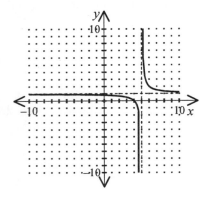

[A] $f(x) = \dfrac{x-3}{x-6}$  [B] $f(x) = \dfrac{x-5}{x-4}$  [C] $f(x) = \dfrac{x-6}{x-3}$  [D] $f(x) = \dfrac{x-4}{x-5}$

[8.2.2.15] *Dynamic Item*

15. Write a rational function that matches the graph.

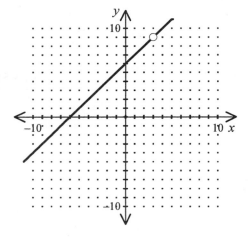

**Lesson 2: Rational Functions and Their Graphs**

[8.2.2.16] *Dynamic Item*

16. Graph the rational function $f(x) = \dfrac{x^2 + x - 30}{x^2 - 2x - 15}$. Identify the vertical and horizontal asymptotes, and any holes in the graph.

**Lesson 3: Multiplying and Dividing Rational Expressions**

Objective 1: Multiply and divide rational expressions.

[8.3.1.17] *Dynamic Item*

17. Simplify the rational expression.

$\dfrac{x^2 + 11x + 28}{x^2 - 16} \div \dfrac{x + 7}{x - 7}$

[A] $\dfrac{11x + 7}{4}$    [B] $\dfrac{x - 11}{x - 4}$    [C] $\dfrac{x + 4}{x - 7}$    [D] $\dfrac{x - 7}{x - 4}$

[8.3.1.18] *Dynamic Item*

18. Simplify the rational expression.

$\dfrac{x^2 - 25}{4x} \cdot \dfrac{9x}{x + 5}$

[A] $\dfrac{9(x - 5)}{4}$    [B] $\dfrac{(x + 5)^2 (x - 5)}{36x^2}$    [C] $\dfrac{9(x + 5)}{4}$    [D] $\dfrac{(x - 5)^2 (x + 5)}{36x^2}$

[8.3.1.19] *Dynamic Item*

19. Simplify the rational expression.

$\dfrac{x - 2}{3x - 2y} \cdot \dfrac{9x^2 - 4y^2}{2x^2 - 9x + 10}$

**Lesson 3: Multiplying and Dividing Rational Expressions**

[8.3.1.20] *Dynamic Item*

20. Simplify the rational expression.

$$\frac{x+5}{x-5} \div \frac{x^2-25}{5-x}$$

Objective 2: Simplify rational expressions, including complex fractions.

[8.3.2.21] *Dynamic Item*

21. Simplify the rational expression.

$$\frac{\dfrac{x^2-16x+64}{-36x}}{\dfrac{x-8}{-6x}}$$

[A] $\dfrac{x+64}{6x}$      [B] $\dfrac{x+8}{6}$      [C] $\dfrac{x-8}{6}$      [D] $-15x-8$

[8.3.2.22] *Dynamic Item*

22. Simplify the rational expression.

$$\frac{\dfrac{2}{x^2-11x+30}+\dfrac{1}{x^2+3x-54}}{\dfrac{2}{x^2+4x-45}+\dfrac{1}{x^2-3x-18}}$$

[A] $\dfrac{(3x+13)(x-3)(x-6)}{3x^2-2x-81}$      [B] $\dfrac{(3x+13)(x+3)}{3x^2-2x-81}$

[C] $\dfrac{(3x+13)(x+3)(x-6)}{3x^2-2x-81}$      [D] $\dfrac{(3x+13)(x-3)}{3x^2-2x-81}$

## Lesson 3: Multiplying and Dividing Rational Expressions

[8.3.2.23] *Dynamic Item*

23. Simplify the rational expression.

$$\dfrac{\dfrac{x^2+6x+9}{24x}}{\dfrac{x+3}{6x}}$$

[8.3.2.24] *Dynamic Item*

24. Simplify the rational expression.

$$\dfrac{x^{-2}y^{-2}z^{-2}-y^{-3}z^2}{-3x^{-3}-xy^3}$$

## Lesson 4: Adding and Subtracting Rational Expressions

Objective 1: Add and subtract rational expressions.

[8.4.1.25] *Dynamic Item*

25. Simplify.

$$\dfrac{4x-7}{x^2-16}-\dfrac{5x-11}{x^2-16}$$

[A] $\dfrac{1}{x+4}$  [B] $-\dfrac{1}{x+4}$  [C] $\dfrac{-x-18}{x^2-16}$  [D] $-\dfrac{1}{x-4}$

[8.4.1.26] *Dynamic Item*

26. Simplify.

$$\dfrac{x-3}{4x^2}-\dfrac{-2x+3}{9x}+\dfrac{5x}{24}$$

[A] $\dfrac{15x^3+16x^2+42x-54}{72x^2}$  [B] $\dfrac{15x^3+16x^2-6x-54}{72x^2}$  [C] $\dfrac{8x+3}{12x^3}$  [D] $\dfrac{8x-3}{12x^3}$

**Lesson 4: Adding and Subtracting Rational Expressions**

[8.4.1.27] *Dynamic Item*

27. Simplify.

$$\frac{-6x-3}{x^2-9} - \frac{-5x-6}{x^2-9}$$

[8.4.1.28] *Dynamic Item*

28. Simplify.

$$\frac{x^{-3} - y^{-1}}{x^{-1} - y^{-3}}$$

**Lesson 5: Solving Rational Equations and Inequalities**

Objective 1: Solve a rational equation or inequality by using algebra, a table, or a graph.

[8.5.1.29] *Dynamic Item*

29. Solve the equation or inequality.

$$\frac{2}{x+2} - \frac{3}{x+3} = 0$$

[A] $x = 0$  [B] $x = \dfrac{12}{5}$  [C] $x = 12$  [D] no solution

[8.5.1.30] *Dynamic Item*

30. Solve the equation or inequality.

$$\frac{2x+2}{x^2-25} \geq \frac{1}{x+5}$$

[A] $x < -5$ or $x \geq 7$  [B] $-5 < x \leq 7$; undefined at $x = 5$

[C] $-7 \leq x < 5$; undefined at $x = -5$  [D] $x \leq -7$ or $x > 5$

**Lesson 5: Solving Rational Equations and Inequalities**

[8.5.1.31] *Dynamic Item*

31. Solve the equation or inequality.

$$\frac{x+7}{x-1} = \frac{x-2}{x-5}$$

[8.5.1.32] *Dynamic Item*

32. Solve the equation or inequality.

$$\frac{x+4}{-4x} \leq \frac{x-6}{-4x-1}$$

Objective 2: Solve problems by using a rational equation or inequality.

[8.5.2.33] *Dynamic Item*

33. After taking 5 quizzes, your average is 77 out of 100. What must your average score be on the next five quizzes to increase your average to 82?

  [A] 79          [B] 87          [C] 84          [D] 85

[8.5.2.34] *Dynamic Item*

34. Write an equation that can be used to solve the problem. Then answer the question asked.
 A group of college students are volunteering for Habitat for Humanity during their spring break. They are putting the finishing touches on a house they built. Working alone, Dale Horton can paint a certain room in 3 hours. Phillip Lekakis can paint the same room in 6 hours. How long will it take them working together to paint the room?

  [A] $\dfrac{x}{3} + \dfrac{x}{6} = 1$ ; 2.00 hr          [B] $\dfrac{3}{6} + x = 1$ ; 4.50 hr

  [C] $\dfrac{3}{x} + \dfrac{6}{x} = 1$ ; 2.25 hr          [D] $3 + 6 = x$ ; 2.13 hr

### Lesson 5: Solving Rational Equations and Inequalities

[8.5.2.35] *Dynamic Item*

35. Write an equation that can be used to solve the problem. Then answer the question asked.
The sum of the reciprocals of two consecutive even integers is $\frac{7}{24}$. Find the two integers.

[8.5.2.36] *Dynamic Item*

36. The sum of the reciprocal of a number and the reciprocal of 9 less than the number is 4 times the reciprocal of the original number. Find the original number.

### Lesson 6: Radical Expressions and Radical Functions

Objective 1: Analyze the graphs of radical functions, and evaluate radical expressions.

[8.6.1.37] *Dynamic Item*

37. Evaluate the radical expression: $-8\left(\sqrt[3]{-125}\right)^2$

   [A] –320      [B] 1600      [C] 40      [D] –200

[8.6.1.38] *Dynamic Item*

38. Find the domain of the radical function.
$f(x) = -\sqrt{3-x}$
   [A] $x \le 3$      [B] $x \le -3\}$      [C] $x \ge 3$      [D] $x \ge -3$

[8.6.1.39] *Dynamic Item*

39. Find the domain of the radical function.
$f(x) = \sqrt{3x-6}$

[8.6.1.40] *Dynamic Item*

40. Evaluate the radical expression: $\frac{1}{7}\left(\sqrt[3]{729}\right)^2$

**Lesson 6:  Radical Expressions and Radical Functions**

Objective 2:  Find the inverse of a quadratic function.

[8.6.2.41]  *Dynamic Item*

41.  Which is the correct inverse of $y = 2x^2 + 3$ and the graph of both $y = 2x^2 + 3$ and its inverse on the same coordinate plane?

[A]

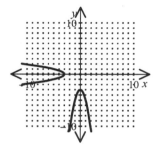

$$y = \pm \frac{\sqrt{-(x+3)}}{2}$$

[B]

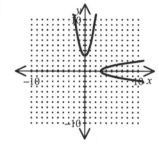

$$y = \pm \sqrt{\frac{x-3}{2}}$$

[C]

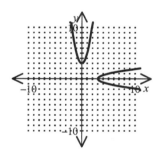

$$y = \pm \frac{\sqrt{x-3}}{2}$$

[D]

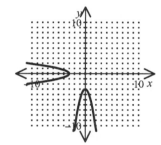

$$y = \pm \sqrt{\frac{-(x+3)}{2}}$$

**Lesson 6: Radical Expressions and Radical Functions**

[8.6.2.42] *Dynamic Item*

42. Which is the correct inverse of $y = -4x^2 - 5$ and the graph of both $y = -4x^2 - 5$ and its inverse on the same coordinate plane?

[A]

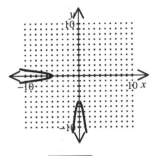

$$y = \pm\sqrt{-\dfrac{x+5}{4}}$$

[B]

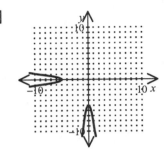

$$y = \pm -\dfrac{\sqrt{x+5}}{4}$$

[C]

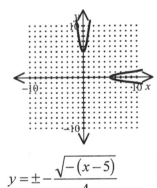

$$y = \pm -\dfrac{\sqrt{-(x-5)}}{4}$$

[D]

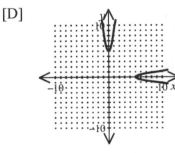

$$y = \pm\sqrt{-\dfrac{-(x-5)}{4}}$$

[8.6.2.43] *Dynamic Item*

43. Find the inverse of the function. Then graph the function and its inverse on the same coordinate plane.

$$y = 4x^2 + 13x$$

**Lesson 6: Radical Expressions and Radical Functions**

[8.6.2.44] *Dynamic Item*

44. Find the inverse of the function. Then graph the function and its inverse on the same coordinate plane.

$$y = 2x^2 - 3x + 4$$

**Lesson 7: Simplifying Radical Expressions**

Objective 1: Add, subtract, multiply, divide, and simplify radical expressions.

[8.7.1.45] *Dynamic Item*

45. Simplify the sum, difference, product, or quotient. Assume that the value of any variable is positive.

$$\sqrt[3]{64x} + 9\sqrt[3]{x^4} - 2\sqrt[3]{x} - 7x\sqrt[3]{x}$$

[A] $2\sqrt[3]{x} + 2x\sqrt[3]{x}$ 　　　　　　　　[B] $2\sqrt[3]{x} + (9 - 7x)\sqrt[3]{x^5}$

[C] $-6\sqrt[3]{x} + 16x\sqrt[3]{x}$ 　　　　　　　[D] $62\sqrt[3]{x} + 2x\sqrt[3]{x}$

[8.7.1.46] *Dynamic Item*

46. Simplify the sum, difference, product, or quotient. Assume that the value of any variable is positive.

$$\frac{\sqrt{72z^2x}}{\sqrt{8zx}}$$

[A] $3\sqrt{z}$ 　　　[B] $\sqrt{72z^2x}$ 　　　[C] $\dfrac{\sqrt{9}}{\sqrt{z}}$ 　　　[D] $\sqrt{z^2}$

[8.7.1.47] *Dynamic Item*

47. Simplify the sum, difference, product, or quotient. Assume that the value of any variable is positive.

$$9^{1/2} - 2\left(6\sqrt{5} + 2\right)$$

**Lesson 7: Simplifying Radical Expressions**

[8.7.1.48] *Dynamic Item*

48. Simplify the sum, difference, product, or quotient. Assume that the value of any variable is positive.

$$\sqrt{8x^5y^2} \cdot \sqrt{6x^3y^2}$$

Objective 2: Rationalize a denominator.

[8.7.2.49] *Dynamic Item*

49. Rationalize the denominator.   [A] $\dfrac{\sqrt{8}}{7}$   [B] $\dfrac{8\sqrt{7}}{49}$   [C] $\dfrac{8\sqrt{7}}{7}$   [D] $8\sqrt{7}$

$$\dfrac{8}{\sqrt{7}}$$

[8.7.2.50] *Dynamic Item*

50. Rationalize the denominator.

$$\dfrac{\sqrt{11}}{3-\sqrt{5}}$$

[A] $\dfrac{11\sqrt{11}+\sqrt{15}}{116}$   [B] $-\dfrac{3\sqrt{11}+\sqrt{55}}{2}$   [C] $\dfrac{5\sqrt{11}+\sqrt{33}}{22}$   [D] $\dfrac{3\sqrt{11}+\sqrt{55}}{4}$

[8.7.2.51] *Dynamic Item*

51. Rationalize the denominator.

$$\sqrt{\dfrac{3}{2}}$$

[8.7.2.52] *Dynamic Item*

52. Rationalize the denominator.

$$\dfrac{\sqrt{5}}{5-\sqrt{2}}$$

**Lesson 8: Solving Radical Equations and Inequalities**

Objective 1: Solve radical equations.

[8.8.1.53] *Dynamic Item*

53. Solve the radical equation. If there is no real solution, write *no solution*.
$$2x = \sqrt{15 + 4x}$$

[A] $-\dfrac{5}{2}$        [B] $\dfrac{3}{5}$        [C] $\dfrac{5}{2}$        [D] no real solution

[8.8.1.54] *Dynamic Item*

54. Solve the radical equation. If there is no real solution, write *no solution*.
$$\sqrt{3x + 5} = \sqrt{2x + 5}$$

[8.8.1.55] *Dynamic Item*

55. Solve the radical equation. If there is no real solution, write *no solution*.
$$3\sqrt{4x - 4} + 2 = \sqrt{36x + 4}$$

[A] $\dfrac{13}{4}$        [B] $\dfrac{17}{4}$        [C] $\dfrac{9}{4}$        [D] no solution

[8.8.1.56] *Dynamic Item*

56. Solve the radical equation. If there is no real solution, write *no solution*.
$$\sqrt[3]{4x + 5} + 9 = 7$$

Objective 2: Solve radical inequalities.

[8.8.2.57] *Dynamic Item*

57. Solve the radical inequality.
$$\sqrt{x + 14} \leq x - 16$$

[A] $-14 \leq x \leq 22$      [B] $x \leq 22$      [C] $x \geq 22$      [D] $x \geq 16$

**Lesson 8:  Solving Radical Equations and Inequalities**

[8.8.2.58]  *Dynamic Item*

58.  Solve the radical inequality.      [A] $x \le 1$     [B] $x \ge 3$     [C] $x \le 3$     [D] $x \ge 1$

$\sqrt[3]{4x - 4} + 7 \ge 9$

[8.8.2.59]  *Dynamic Item*

59.  Solve the radical inequality.

$\sqrt{x + 13} \le 13 - \sqrt{x}$

[8.8.2.60]  *Dynamic Item*

60.  Solve the radical inequality.

$\sqrt{x + 2} - 8 \ge -6$

**Lesson 1: Inverse, Joint, and Combined Variation**

Objective 1: Identify inverse, joint, and combined variations, find the constant of variation, and write an equation for the variation.

[8.1.1.1] *Dynamic Item*

[1] [A]

[8.1.1.2] *Dynamic Item*

[2] [B]

[8.1.1.3] *Dynamic Item*

[3] $y = \dfrac{5}{x}; \dfrac{5}{8}$

[8.1.1.4] *Dynamic Item*

[4] $y = \dfrac{7wx}{z}; 63$

Objective 2: Solve real-world problems involving inverse, joint, or combined variation.

[8.1.2.5] *Dynamic Item*

[5] [C]

[8.1.2.6] *Dynamic Item*

[6] [C]

[8.1.2.7] *Dynamic Item*

[7] $13.49

[8.1.2.8] *Dynamic Item*

[8] 90 barrels

## Lesson 2: Rational Functions and Their Graphs

Objective 1: Identify and evaluate rational functions.

[8.2.1.9] *Dynamic Item*

[9] [D]

[8.2.1.10] *Dynamic Item*

[10] [C]

[8.2.1.11] *Dynamic Item*

[11] rational; $x \neq 3$ or $-1$; asymptotes at $y = \dfrac{2}{3}$ and $x = -1$; hole at $x = 3$

[8.2.1.12] *Dynamic Item*

[12] rational; $x \neq -\dfrac{4}{7}$; asymptotes at $y = \dfrac{6}{7}$, and $x = -\dfrac{4}{7}$

Objective 2: Graph a rational function, find its domain, write equations for its asymptotes, and identify any holes in its graph.

[8.2.2.13] *Dynamic Item*

[13] [B]

[8.2.2.14] *Dynamic Item*

[14] [D]

## Algebra 2
180

[8.2.2.15]  *Dynamic Item*

[15]  $f(x) = \dfrac{x^2 + 3x - 18}{x - 3}$

[8.2.2.16]  *Dynamic Item*

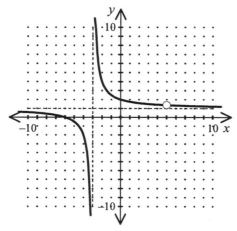

[16]  asymptotes: $y = 1$, $x = -3$; hole at $x = 5$

**Lesson 3:  Multiplying and Dividing Rational Expressions**

Objective 1:  Multiply and divide rational expressions.

[8.3.1.17]  *Dynamic Item*

[17]  [D]

[8.3.1.18]  *Dynamic Item*

[18]  [A]

[8.3.1.19]  *Dynamic Item*

[19]  $\dfrac{3x + 2y}{2x - 5}$

Algebra 2

[8.3.1.20] *Dynamic Item*

[20] $\dfrac{1}{5-x}$

Objective 2: Simplify rational expressions, including complex fractions.

[8.3.2.21] *Dynamic Item*

[21] [C]

[8.3.2.22] *Dynamic Item*

[22] [B]

[8.3.2.23] *Dynamic Item*

[23] $\dfrac{x+3}{4}$

[8.3.2.24] *Dynamic Item*

[24] $\dfrac{xy-x^3z^4}{-3y^3z^2-x^4y^6z^2}$

**Lesson 4: Adding and Subtracting Rational Expressions**

Objective 1: Add and subtract rational expressions.

[8.4.1.25] *Dynamic Item*

[25] [B]

[8.4.1.26] *Dynamic Item*

[26] [B]

[8.4.1.27] *Dynamic Item*

[27] $-\dfrac{1}{x+3}$

[8.4.1.28] *Dynamic Item*

[28] $\dfrac{y^3 - x^3y^2}{x^2y^3 - x^3}$

**Lesson 5: Solving Rational Equations and Inequalities**

Objective 1: Solve a rational equation or inequality by using algebra, a table, or a graph.

[8.5.1.29] *Dynamic Item*

[29] [A]

[8.5.1.30] *Dynamic Item*

[30] [D]

[8.5.1.31] *Dynamic Item*

[31] $x = \dfrac{37}{5}$

[8.5.1.32] *Dynamic Item*

[32] $-\dfrac{1}{4} < x \le -\dfrac{4}{41},\ x > 0$

Objective 2: Solve problems by using a rational equation or inequality.

[8.5.2.33] *Dynamic Item*

[33] [B]

[8.5.2.34] *Dynamic Item*

[34] [A]

[8.5.2.35] *Dynamic Item*

[35] $\dfrac{1}{x} + \dfrac{1}{x+2} = \dfrac{7}{24}$; 6 and 8

[8.5.2.36] *Dynamic Item*

[36] $\dfrac{27}{2}$

**Lesson 6: Radical Expressions and Radical Functions**

Objective 1: Analyze the graphs of radical functions, and evaluate radical expressions.

[8.6.1.37] *Dynamic Item*

[37] [D]

[8.6.1.38] *Dynamic Item*

[38] [A]

[8.6.1.39] *Dynamic Item*

[39] $x \geq 2$

[8.6.1.40] *Dynamic Item*

[40] $\dfrac{81}{7}$

Objective 2: Find the inverse of a quadratic function.

[8.6.2.41] *Dynamic Item*

[41]  [B]

[8.6.2.42] *Dynamic Item*

[42]  [A]

[8.6.2.43] *Dynamic Item*

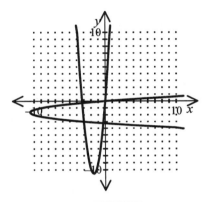

[43]  $y = \dfrac{-13 \pm \sqrt{16x + 169}}{8}$

[8.6.2.44] *Dynamic Item*

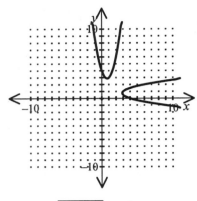

[44] $\quad y = \dfrac{3 \pm \sqrt{8x - 23}}{4}$

## Lesson 7: Simplifying Radical Expressions

Objective 1: Add, subtract, multiply, divide, and simplify radical expressions.

[8.7.1.45] *Dynamic Item*

[45] [A]

[8.7.1.46] *Dynamic Item*

[46] [A]

[8.7.1.47] *Dynamic Item*

[47] $\quad -1 - 12\sqrt{5}$

[8.7.1.48] *Dynamic Item*

[48] $\quad 4x^4 y^2 \sqrt{3}$

Objective 2: Rationalize a denominator.

[8.7.2.49] *Dynamic Item*

[49]  [C]

[8.7.2.50] *Dynamic Item*

[50]  [D]

[8.7.2.51] *Dynamic Item*

[51]  $\dfrac{\sqrt{6}}{2}$

[8.7.2.52] *Dynamic Item*

[52]  $\dfrac{5\sqrt{5} + \sqrt{10}}{23}$

**Lesson 8: Solving Radical Equations and Inequalities**

Objective 1: Solve radical equations.

[8.8.1.53] *Dynamic Item*

[53]  [C]

[8.8.1.54] *Dynamic Item*

[54]  0

[8.8.1.55] *Dynamic Item*

[55]  [A]

[8.8.1.56] *Dynamic Item*

[56] $-\dfrac{13}{4}$

Objective 2: Solve radical inequalities.

[8.8.2.57] *Dynamic Item*

[57] [C]

[8.8.2.58] *Dynamic Item*

[58] [B]

[8.8.2.59] *Dynamic Item*

[59] $0 \le x \le 36$

[8.8.2.60] *Dynamic Item*

[60] $x \ge 2$

**Lesson 1: Introduction to Conic Sections**

Objective 1: Classify a conic section as the intersection of a plane and a double cone.

[9.1.1.1]  *Dynamic Item*

1.  Identify the conic section produced by the intersection of the plane and the cones in the following diagram.

[A] parabola          [B] ellipse          [C] circle          [D] hyperbola

[9.1.1.2]  *Dynamic Item*

2.  Which of the following conic section diagrams produces the circle below?

[A]

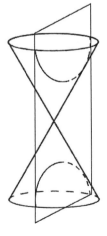

## Lesson 1: Introduction to Conic Sections

[B]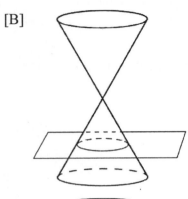

[C]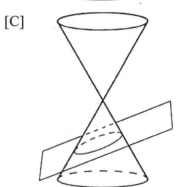

[D]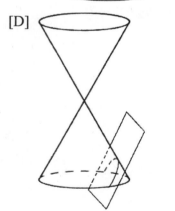

**Lesson 1: Introduction to Conic Sections**

[9.1.1.3]  *Dynamic Item*

3.  Identify the conic section produced by the following diagram.

[9.1.1.4]  *Dynamic Item*

4.  Draw a plane on the following diagram so that the conic section formed by the intersection of the plane and the cones is a circle.

**Lesson 1: Introduction to Conic Sections**

Objective 2: Use the distance and midpoint formulas.

[9.1.2.5] *Dynamic Item*

5. Find the distance between points $E(6, 5)$ and $A(-1, 6)$, and the coordinates of the midpoint of $\overline{EA}$.

[A] distance $= 5\sqrt{2}$; 7.07

midpoint $= \left(\dfrac{5}{2}, \dfrac{11}{2}\right)$

[B] distance $= 5\sqrt{2}$; 7.07

midpoint $= \left(\dfrac{7}{2}, -\dfrac{1}{2}\right)$

[C] distance $= \sqrt{146}$; 12.08

midpoint $= \left(\dfrac{5}{2}, \dfrac{11}{2}\right)$

[D] distance $= \sqrt{146}$; 12.08

midpoint $= \left(\dfrac{7}{2}, -\dfrac{1}{2}\right)$

[9.1.2.6] *Dynamic Item*

6. Find the center and the radius of the circle that has a diameter with the given endpoints.
   Diameter $\overline{CD}$, $C(6, -3)$, $D(-4, 7)$

[A] center: $(1, 2)$

radius: $5\sqrt{2}$ ; 7.07

[B] center: $(1, 2)$

radius: $2\sqrt{13}$ ; 7.21

[C] center: $(5, -5)$

radius: $\sqrt{185}$ ; 13.6

[D] center: $(5, -5)$

radius: $\sqrt{187}$ ; 13.67

[9.1.2.7] *Dynamic Item*

7. Find the center and the radius of the circle that has a diameter with the given endpoints.
   Diameter $\overline{CD}$, with endpoints $C(1, 1)$, $D(-5, 3)$

[9.1.2.8] *Dynamic Item*

8. Find the distance between points $B(2, 4)$ and $G(8, 1)$, and the coordinates of the midpoint of $\overline{BG}$.

**Lesson 2: Parabolas**

Objective 1: Write and graph the standard equation of a parabola given sufficient information.

[9.2.1.9] *Dynamic Item*

9.  Find the standard equation and graph of a parabola that matches the given set of characteristics.

    focus: $(-3, 9)$

    vertex: $(-3, 4)$

[A]

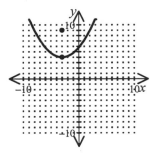

$$y - 4 = \frac{1}{5}(x + 3)^2$$

[B]

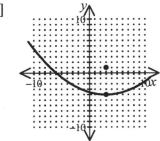

$$y - 4 = -\frac{1}{20}(x + 3)^2$$

[C]

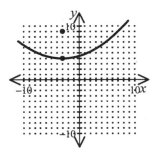

$$y - 4 = \frac{1}{20}(x + 3)^2$$

[D]

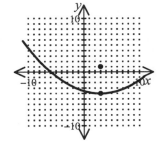

$$y + 4 = \frac{1}{20}(x - 3)^2$$

**Lesson 2:  Parabolas**

[9.2.1.10]  *Dynamic Item*

10.  Find the standard equation and graph of a parabola that matches the given set of characteristics.

   vertex: $(0,\ 0)$

   focus: $(0, 2)$

[A]
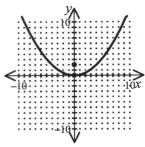

$$y = \frac{1}{8}x^2$$

[B]
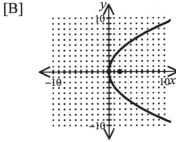

$$x = \frac{1}{8}y^2$$

[C]
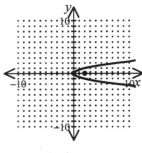

$$y = -2x^2$$

[D]
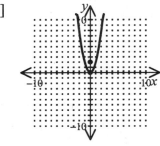

$$y = 2x^2$$

[9.2.1.11]  *Dynamic Item*

11.  Write the standard equation for the parabola with the given set of characteristics. Then graph the parabola.

   focus: $(2,\ 7)$

   vertex: $(2,\ 6)$

**Lesson 2: Parabolas**

[9.2.1.12] *Dynamic Item*

12. Write the standard equation for the parabola with the given set of characteristics. Then graph the parabola.

    axis of symmetry: $y = 0$

    focus: $(6, \ 0)$

    vertex: $(0, \ 0)$

Objective 2: Given an equation of a parabola, graph it and label the vertex, focus, and directrix.

[9.2.2.13] *Dynamic Item*

13. Find the vertex, focus, and directrix and the correct graph $x = \dfrac{1}{8}(y - 8)^2 + 7$.

    [A]  vertex: (–7, 8),
         focus : (–5, 8),
         directrix is $x = 5$

    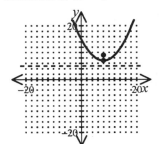

    [B]  vertex: (–7, 8),
         focus : (9, –8),
         directrix is $x = 5$

    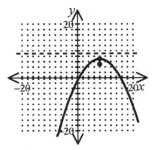

    [C]  vertex: (7, 8),
         focus : (9, 8),
         directrix is $x = 5$

    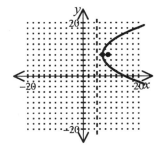

    [D]  vertex: (7, 8),
         focus : (–5, –8),
         directrix is $x = -5$

    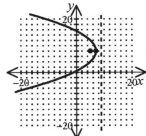

**Lesson 2: Parabolas**

[9.2.2.14]  *Dynamic Item*

14.  Find the vertex, focus, and directrix and the correct graph of the equation
$8(x + 3) = (y - 1)^2$.

[A]  vertex: $(-3, 1)$
focus: $(-1, 1)$
directrix: $x = -5$

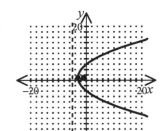

[B]  vertex: $(-3, 1)$
focus: $(-5, 1)$
directrix: $x = -1$

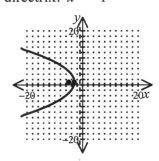

[C]  vertex: $(1, -3)$
focus: $(1, -5)$
directrix: $y = -5$

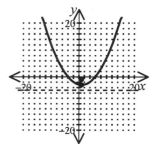

[D]  vertex: $(1, -3)$
focus: $(1, -5)$
directrix: $y = -1$

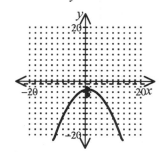

[9.2.2.15]  *Dynamic Item*

15.  Find the vertex, focus, and directrix. Then draw the graph.
$x^2 + 8x = -4y - 28$

**Lesson 2: Parabolas**

[9.2.2.16] *Dynamic Item*

16. Find the vertex, focus, and directrix. Then draw the graph.

$$y = -\frac{1}{32}(x-1)^2 + 4$$

**Lesson 3: Circles**

Objective 1: Write an equation for a circle given sufficient information.

[9.3.1.17] *Dynamic Item*

17. Find the standard equation of a circle with the given radius and center.
    radius: 6
    center: $(0, \ 0)$

[A] $\dfrac{x^2}{12} + \dfrac{x^2}{12} = 1$     [B] $x^2 + y^2 = 12$     [C] $x^2 + y^2 = 6$     [D] $x^2 + y^2 = 36$

[9.3.1.18] *Dynamic Item*

18. Find the standard equation of a circle with the given radius and center.
    radius: 4
    center: $(5, \ 4)$

[A] $(x+5)^2 - (y+4)^2 = 4$        [B] $(x-5)^2 + (y+4)^2 = 16$

[C] $(x-5)^2 + (y-4)^2 = 16$       [D] $(x+5)^2 + (y+4)^2 = 4$

[9.3.1.19] *Dynamic Item*

19. Find the standard equation of a circle with the given radius and center.
    radius: 6
    center: $(3, \ 4)$

**Lesson 3: Circles**

[9.3.1.20]  *Dynamic Item*

20.  Write the standard equation of the circle in the graph.

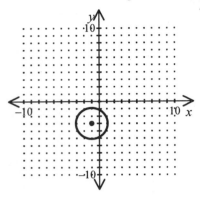

Objective 2:  Given an equation of a circle, graph it and label the radius and the center.

[9.3.2.21]  *Dynamic Item*

21.  Which is the graph of the equation $(x + 2)^2 + (y + 1)^2 = 25$ with the correct center and radius?

[A]

center: $(1,\ 2)$; radius: 5

**Lesson 3: Circles**

[B]

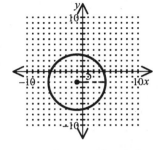

center: $(-1, -2)$; radius: 5

[C]

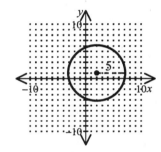

center: $(2, 1)$; radius: 5

[D]

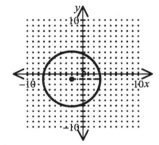

center: $(-2, -1)$; radius: 5

**Lesson 3: Circles**

[9.3.2.22] *Dynamic Item*

22. Which is the graph and the standard form of the equation $x^2 + y^2 + 2x + 8y + 13 = 0$?

[A]

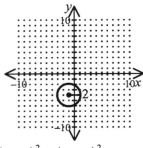

$(x+1)^2 + (y+4)^2 = 4$

center: $(-1, -4)$; radius: 2

[B]

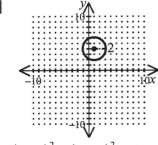

$(x-1)^2 + (y-4)^2 = 4$

center: $(1, 4)$; radius: 2

[C]

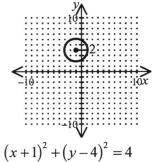

$(x+1)^2 + (y-4)^2 = 4$

center: $(-1, 4)$; radius: 2

[D]

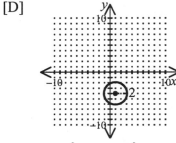

$(x-1)^2 + (y+4)^2 = 4$

center: $(1, -4)$; radius: 2

[9.3.2.23] *Dynamic Item*

23. Graph the equation $(x+2)^2 + (y+3)^2 = 9$. Label the center and the radius.

[9.3.2.24] *Dynamic Item*

24. Write the equation $x^2 + y^2 + 4x - 6y + 13 = 16$ in standard form and then graph the result. Label the center and the radius.

### Algebra 2
200

**Lesson 4: Ellipses**

Objective 1: Write the standard equation for an ellipse given sufficient information.

[9.4.1.25]  *Dynamic Item*

25.  Find the standard equation for the ellipse, using either the given characteristics, or characteristics taken from the graph.

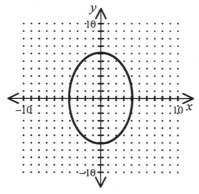

[A] $\dfrac{x^2}{16} + \dfrac{y^2}{36} = 1$     [B] $\dfrac{x^2}{36} + \dfrac{y^2}{16} = 1$     [C] $\dfrac{x^2}{6} + \dfrac{y^2}{4} = 1$     [D] $\dfrac{x^2}{4} + \dfrac{y^2}{6} = 1$

[9.4.1.26]  *Dynamic Item*

26.  Find the standard equation for the ellipse, using either the given characteristics, or characteristics taken from the graph.

vertices: $\left(0, \ \pm 9\right)$; foci: $\left(0, \ \pm 2\sqrt{14}\ \right)$

[A] $\dfrac{x^2}{81} + \dfrac{y^2}{56} = 1$     [B] $\dfrac{x^2}{25} + \dfrac{y^2}{81} = 1$     [C] $\dfrac{x^2}{56} + \dfrac{y^2}{81} = 1$     [D] $\dfrac{x^2}{81} + \dfrac{y^2}{25} = 1$

**Lesson 4:  Ellipses**

[9.4.1.27]  *Dynamic Item*

27.  Find the standard equation for the ellipse, using either the given characteristics, or characteristics taken from the graph.

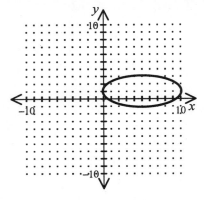

[9.4.1.28]  *Dynamic Item*

28.  Find the standard equation for the ellipse, using either the given characteristics, or characteristics taken from the graph.

vertices: $(\pm 7,\ 0)$; foci: $\left(\pm 2\sqrt{10},\ 0\right)$

**Lesson 4: Ellipses**

Objective 2: Given an equation of an ellipse, graph it and label the center, vertices, co-vertices, and foci.

[9.4.2.29]  *Dynamic Item*

29.  Which is the graph of the ellipse represented by the equation $\dfrac{(x-1)^2}{9} + \dfrac{(y-5)^2}{16} = 1$?

[A]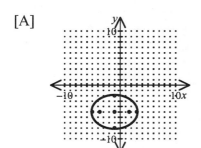

center: $(-1, -5)$
foci: $(-3.65, -5), (1.65, -5)$
vertices: $(-5, -5), (3, -5)$
co-vert.: $(-1, -8), (-1, -2)$

[B]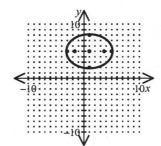

center: $(1, 5)$
foci: $(-1.65, 5), (3.65, 5)$
vertices: $(-3, 5), (5, 5)$
co-vert.: $(1, 2), (1, 8)$

[C]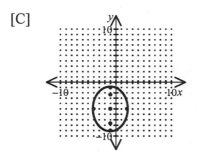

center: $(-1, -5)$
foci: $(-1, -7.65), (-1, -2.35)$
vertices: $(-1, -9), (-1, -1)$
co-vert.: $(-4, -5), (2, -5)$

[D]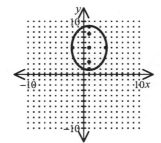

center: $(1, 5)$
foci: $(1, 2.35), (1, 7.65)$
vertices: $(1, 1), (1, 9)$
co-vert.: $(-2, 5), (4, 5)$

**Lesson 4: Ellipses**

[9.4.2.30] *Dynamic Item*

30. Which is the graph of the ellipse represented by the equation
$16x^2 + 25y^2 + 160x + 50y + 25 = 0$, together with the standard form of the equation?

[A]

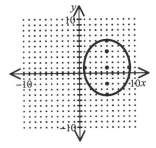

$$\frac{(x-5)^2}{25} + \frac{(y-1)^2}{16} = 1$$

center: $(5,\ 1)$

foci: $(5,\ -2),\ (5,\ 4)$

vertices: $(5,\ -4),\ (5,\ 6)$

co-vert.: $(1,\ 1),\ (9,\ 1)$

[B]

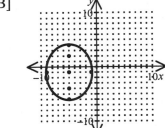

$$\frac{(x+5)^2}{25} + \frac{(y+1)^2}{16} = 1$$

center: $(-5,\ -1)$

foci: $(-5,\ -4),\ (-5,\ 2)$

vertices: $(-5,\ -6),\ (-5,\ 4)$

co-vert.: $(-9,\ -1),\ (-1,\ -1)$

[C]

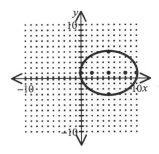

$$\frac{(x-5)^2}{16} + \frac{(y-1)^2}{25} = 1$$

center: $(5,\ 1)$

foci: $(2,\ 1),\ (8,\ 1)$

vertices: $(0,\ 1),\ (10,\ 1)$

co-vert.: $(5,\ -3),\ (5,\ 5)$

[D]

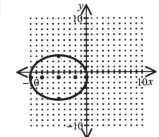

$$\frac{(x+5)^2}{16} + \frac{(y+1)^2}{25} = 1$$

center: $(-5,\ -1)$

foci: $(-8,\ -1),\ (-2,\ -1)$

vertices: $(-10,\ -1),\ (0,\ -1)$

co-vert.: $(-5,\ -5),\ (-5,\ 3)$

## Algebra 2
204

## Lesson 4: Ellipses

[9.4.2.31] *Dynamic Item*

31. Write the equation $4x^2 + 16y^2 + 32x + 96y + 144 = 0$ in standard form and then graph the ellipse. Label the center, foci, vertices, and co-vertices.

[9.4.2.32] *Dynamic Item*

32. Graph the equation $\dfrac{(x-5)^2}{25} + \dfrac{(y+5)^2}{16} = 1$. Label the center, foci, vertices, and co-vertices.

## Lesson 5: Hyperbolas

Objective 1: Write the standard equation for a hyperbola given sufficient information.

[9.5.1.33] *Dynamic Item*

33. Find the standard equation for the hyperbola with the given characteristics.
    vertices: $(4,\ 0)$ and $(-4,\ 0)$
    asymptote: $y = \dfrac{5}{4}x$

[A] $\dfrac{x^2}{16} - \dfrac{y^2}{25} = 1$     [B] $\dfrac{x^2}{25} - \dfrac{y^2}{9} = 1$     [C] $\dfrac{x^2}{16} - \dfrac{y^2}{9} = 1$     [D] $\dfrac{x^2}{9} - \dfrac{y^2}{16} = 1$

[9.5.1.34] *Dynamic Item*

34. Find the standard equation for the hyperbola with the given characteristics.
    center: $(4,\ -4)$
    one focus: $(9,\ -4)$
    one vertex: $(7,\ -4)$

[A] $\dfrac{(x+4)^2}{9} - \dfrac{(y-4)^2}{16} = 1$     [B] $\dfrac{(x-4)^2}{9} - \dfrac{(y+4)^2}{16} = 1$

[C] $\dfrac{(x-4)^2}{9} + \dfrac{(y+4)^2}{16} = 1$     [D] $\dfrac{(y+4)^2}{9} - \dfrac{(x-4)^2}{16} = 1$

**Lesson 5:  Hyperbolas**

[9.5.1.35]  *Dynamic Item*

35.  Find the standard equation for the hyperbola with the given characteristics.

vertices: $(3, 0)$ and $(-3, 0)$

asymptote: $y = \dfrac{4}{3}x$

[9.5.1.36]  *Dynamic Item*

36.  The two hyperbolas in the graph are conjugates, meaning they share the same asymptotes. Given the following equation of the hyperbola represented by the thin curve, find the equation of its conjugate, which is represented by the thick curve.

$$\frac{x^2}{9} - \frac{y^2}{25} = 1$$

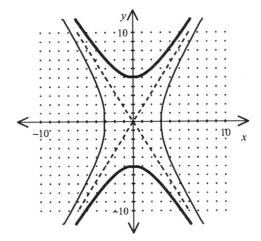

**Lesson 5: Hyperbolas**

Objective 2: Graph the equation of a hyperbola, and identify the center, foci, vertices, and co-vertices.

[9.5.2.37] *Dynamic Item*

37. For the equation of a hyperbola, find the standard equation, vertices, foci, asymptotes, and correct graph.

$$16y^2 - 4x^2 - 64 = 0$$

[A] $\dfrac{y^2}{16} - \dfrac{x^2}{4} = 1$

vertices: $(0,\ 4),\ (0,\ -4)$

foci: $\left(0,\ 2\sqrt{5}\right),\ \left(0,\ -2\sqrt{5}\right)$

asymptotes: $y = 2x,\ y = -2x$

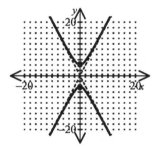

[B] $\dfrac{x^2}{4} - \dfrac{y^2}{16} = 1$

vertices: $(2,\ 0),\ (-2,\ 0)$

foci: $\left(-2\sqrt{5},\ 0\right),\ \left(2\sqrt{5},\ 0\right)$

asymptotes: $y = 2x,\ y = -2x$

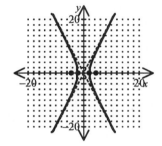

[C] $\dfrac{x^2}{16} - \dfrac{y^2}{4} = 1$

vertices: $(4,\ 0),\ (-4,\ -4)$

foci: $\left(-2\sqrt{5},\ 0\right),\ \left(2\sqrt{5},\ 0\right)$

asymptotes: $y = \dfrac{1}{2}x,\ y = -\dfrac{1}{2}x$

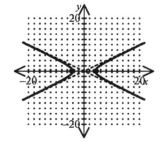

[D] $\dfrac{x^2}{4} - \dfrac{y^2}{16} = 1$

vertices: $(2,\ 0),\ (0,\ -2)$

foci: $\left(0,\ 2\sqrt{5}\right),\ \left(0,\ -2\sqrt{5}\right)$

asymptotes: $y = \dfrac{1}{2}x,\ y = -\dfrac{1}{2}x$

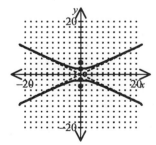

**Lesson 5: Hyperbolas**

[9.5.2.38]  *Dynamic Item*

38.  For the equation of a hyperbola, find the standard equation, vertices, foci, asymptotes, and correct graph.

$$25y^2 - 9x^2 - 225 = 0$$

[A]  $\dfrac{x^2}{25} - \dfrac{y^2}{9} = 1$

vertices: $(5, 0)$, $(-5, 0)$

foci: $\left(\sqrt{34}, 0\right)$, $\left(-\sqrt{34}, 0\right)$

asymptotes: $y = \dfrac{3}{5}x$, $y = -\dfrac{3}{5}x$

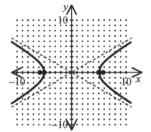

[B]  $\dfrac{x^2}{9} - \dfrac{y^2}{25} = 1$

vertices: $(3, 0)$, $(-3, 0)$

foci: $\left(\sqrt{34}, 0\right)$, $\left(-\sqrt{34}, 0\right)$

asymptotes: $y = \dfrac{5}{3}x$, $y = -\dfrac{5}{3}x$

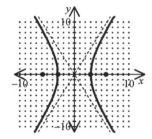

[C]  $\dfrac{y^2}{9} - \dfrac{x^2}{25} = 1$

vertices: $(0, 3)$, $(0, -3)$

foci: $\left(0, \sqrt{34}\right)$, $\left(0, -\sqrt{34}\right)$

asymptotes: $y = \dfrac{3}{5}x$, $y = -\dfrac{3}{5}x$

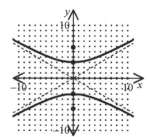

[D]  $\dfrac{y^2}{25} - \dfrac{x^2}{9} = 1$

vertices: $(0, 5)$, $(0, -5)$

foci: $\left(0, \sqrt{34}\right)$, $\left(0, -\sqrt{34}\right)$

asymptotes: $y = \dfrac{5}{3}x$, $y = -\dfrac{5}{3}x$

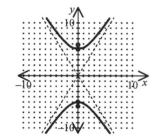

### Lesson 5: Hyperbolas

[9.5.2.39] *Dynamic Item*

39. For the equation of a hyperbola, find the standard equation, vertices, foci, asymptotes, and graph.

$$\frac{x^2}{49} - \frac{y^2}{36} = 1$$

[9.5.2.40] *Dynamic Item*

40. For the equation of a hyperbola, find the standard equation, vertices, foci, asymptotes, and graph.

$$16y^2 - 9x^2 - 144 = 0$$

### Lesson 6: Solving Nonlinear Systems

Objective 1: Solve a system of equations involving first- or second-degree equations in two variables.

[9.6.1.41] *Dynamic Item*

41. Solve the nonlinear system of equations.

$$\begin{cases} x^2 + y^2 = 36 \\ x + y = 6 \end{cases}$$

[A] one solution: $\left(3\sqrt{2}, \, 3\sqrt{2}\right)$     [B] two solutions: $\left(3\sqrt{2}, \, 3\sqrt{2}\right)$ and $\left(-3\sqrt{2}, \, -3\sqrt{2}\right)$

[C] four solutions: $\left(0, \, \pm 6\right)$ and $\left(\pm 6, \, 0\right)$     [D] two solutions: $\left(0, \, 6\right)$ and $\left(6, \, 0\right)$

[9.6.1.42] *Dynamic Item*

42. Solve the nonlinear system of equations.

$$\begin{cases} x^2 + y^2 = 20 \\ x^2 - 2y^2 = 8 \end{cases}$$

[A] four solutions: $\left(\pm 2\sqrt{5}, \, \pm\sqrt{6}\right)$     [B] four solutions: $\left(\pm 2\sqrt{2}, \, 0\right)$ and $\left(0, \, \pm 2\sqrt{5}\right)$

[C] four solutions: $\left(\pm 4, \, \pm 2\right)$     [D] four solutions: $\left(\pm 2, \, \pm 4\right)$

**Lesson 6:  Solving Nonlinear Systems**

[9.6.1.43]  *Dynamic Item*

43.  Solve the nonlinear system of equations.

$$\begin{cases} x^2 + y^2 = 9 \\ x + y = 3 \end{cases}$$

[9.6.1.44]  *Dynamic Item*

44.  Solve the nonlinear system of equations.

$$\begin{cases} x^2 + y^2 = 144 \\ x^2 - 4y^2 = 64 \end{cases}$$

Objective 2:  Identify a conic section from its equation.

[9.6.2.45]  *Dynamic Item*

45.  Which equation describes a circle?

[A] $4x^2 - 3x + 4y^2 + 3y - 3 = 0$      [B] $5y^2 - 3y - 12x^2 + 4x + 3 = 0$

[C] $3x^2 - 3x + 6y^2 - 3y = -2$      [D] $3y^2 - 3x - 3y = -13$

[9.6.2.46]  *Dynamic Item*

46.  Write the equation in standard form and classify the conic section it defines.
$3x^2 + y^2 - 18x + 8y + 40 = 0$

[A] $(x-3)^2 - (y-3)^2 = 1$; hyperbola      [B] $(x-3)^2 + \dfrac{(y+4)^2}{3} = 1$; ellipse

[C] $(x-3)^2 + (y-3)^2 = 1$; parabola      [D] $(x+4)^2 - \dfrac{(y+4)^2}{3} = 1$; circle

[9.6.2.47]  *Dynamic Item*

47.  Write the equation in standard form and classify the conic section it defines.
$4x^2 + 4y^2 + 8x + 8y + 4 = 0$

**Lesson 6:  Solving Nonlinear Systems**

[9.6.2.48]  *Dynamic Item*

48.   Write the equation in standard form and classify the conic section it defines.
$$2x^2 - 4y^2 + 16x + 40y - 76 = 0$$

**Lesson 1: Introduction to Conic Sections**

Objective 1: Classify a conic section as the intersection of a plane and a double cone.

[9.1.1.1] *Dynamic Item*

[1]  [A]

[9.1.1.2] *Dynamic Item*

[2]  [B]

[9.1.1.3] *Dynamic Item*

[3]  parabola

[9.1.1.4] *Dynamic Item*

Answers may vary. Example:

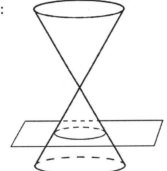

[4]

Objective 2: Use the distance and midpoint formulas.

[9.1.2.5] *Dynamic Item*

[5]  [A]

[9.1.2.6] *Dynamic Item*

[6]  [A]

[9.1.2.7]  *Dynamic Item*

center: $(-2, 2)$

[7]  radius: $\sqrt{10}$ ; 3.16

[9.1.2.8]  *Dynamic Item*

distance $= 3\sqrt{5}$;  6.71

[8]  midpoint $= \left(5, \dfrac{5}{2}\right)$

**Lesson 2:  Parabolas**

Objective 1:  Write and graph the standard equation of a parabola given sufficient information.

[9.2.1.9]  *Dynamic Item*

[9]  [C]

[9.2.1.10]  *Dynamic Item*

[10]  [A]

[9.2.1.11]  *Dynamic Item*

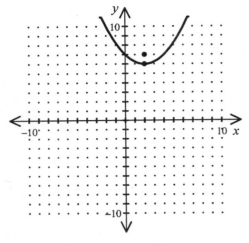

[11]  $y - 6 = \dfrac{1}{4}(x-2)^2$

[9.2.1.12]  *Dynamic Item*

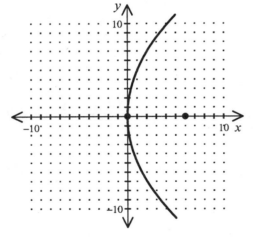

[12]  $x = \dfrac{1}{24}y^2$

Objective 2:  Given an equation of a parabola, graph it and label the vertex, focus, and directrix.

[9.2.2.13]  *Dynamic Item*

[13]  [C]

[9.2.2.14]  *Dynamic Item*

[14]  [A]

[9.2.2.15]  *Dynamic Item*

vertex $= (-4, -3)$; focus $= (-4, -4)$; directrix: $y = -2$

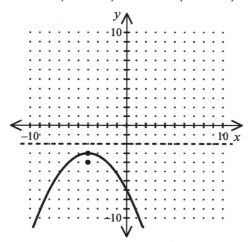

[15]

Algebra 2
**215**

[9.2.2.16]  *Dynamic Item*

vertex: $(1, 4)$; focus: $(1, -4)$; directrix: $y = 12$

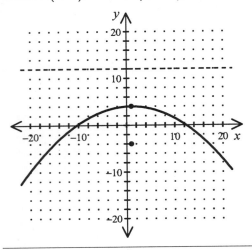

[16] _____

**Lesson 3: Circles**

Objective 1:  Write an equation for a circle given sufficient information.

[9.3.1.17]  *Dynamic Item*

[17]  [D] _____

[9.3.1.18]  *Dynamic Item*

[18]  [C] _____

[9.3.1.19]  *Dynamic Item*

[19]  $(x-3)^2 + (y-4)^2 = 36$ _____

[9.3.1.20]  *Dynamic Item*

[20]  $(x+1)^2 + (y+3)^2 = 4$ _____

Objective 2: Given an equation of a circle, graph it and label the radius and the center.

[9.3.2.21]  *Dynamic Item*

[21]  [D]

[9.3.2.22]  *Dynamic Item*

[22]  [A]

[9.3.2.23]  *Dynamic Item*

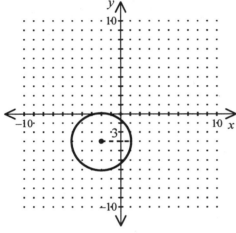

[23]  center: $(-2, -3)$; radius: 3

[9.3.2.24]  *Dynamic Item*

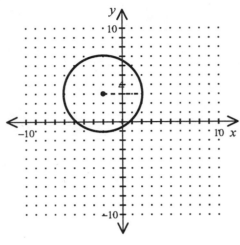

$$(x+2)^2 + (y-3)^2 = 16$$

[24]  center: $(-2, 3)$; radius: 4

**Lesson 4:  Ellipses**

Objective 1:  Write the standard equation for an ellipse given sufficient information.

[9.4.1.25]  *Dynamic Item*

[25]  [A]

[9.4.1.26]  *Dynamic Item*

[26]  [B]

[9.4.1.27]  *Dynamic Item*

[27]  $\dfrac{(x-5)^2}{25} + \dfrac{(y-1)^2}{4} = 1$

[9.4.1.28]  *Dynamic Item*

[28]  $\dfrac{x^2}{49} + \dfrac{y^2}{9} = 1$

Objective 2:  Given an equation of an ellipse, graph it and label the center, vertices, co-vertices, and foci.

[9.4.2.29]  *Dynamic Item*

[29]  [D]

[9.4.2.30]  *Dynamic Item*

[30]  [D]

[9.4.2.31]  *Dynamic Item*

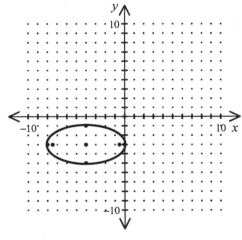

$\dfrac{(x+4)^2}{4} + \dfrac{(y+3)^2}{16} = 1$

center: $(-4, -3)$, foci: $(-7.46, -3)$ and $(-0.54, -3)$

[31]  vertices: $(-8, -3)$ and $(0, -3)$, co-vertices: $(-4, -5)$ and $(-4, -1)$

[9.4.2.32] *Dynamic Item*

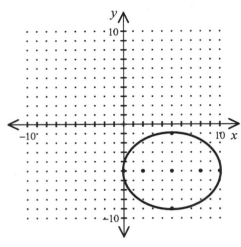

center: $(5, -5)$, foci: $(2, -5)$ and $(8, -5)$

[32]   vertices: $(0, -5)$ and $(10, -5)$, co-vertices: $(5, -9)$ and $(5, -1)$

## Lesson 5: Hyperbolas

Objective 1: Write the standard equation for a hyperbola given sufficient information.

[9.5.1.33] *Dynamic Item*

[33]   [A]

[9.5.1.34] *Dynamic Item*

[34]   [B]

[9.5.1.35] *Dynamic Item*

[35]   $\dfrac{x^2}{9} - \dfrac{y^2}{16} = 1$

[9.5.1.36] *Dynamic Item*

[36]   $\dfrac{y^2}{25} - \dfrac{x^2}{9} = 1$

Objective 2:  Graph the equation of a hyperbola, and identify the center, foci, vertices, and co-vertices.

[9.5.2.37]  *Dynamic Item*

[37]  [D]

[9.5.2.38]  *Dynamic Item*

[38]  [C]

[9.5.2.39]  *Dynamic Item*

vertices: $(\pm 7, 0)$, foci: $\left(\pm \sqrt{85}, 0\right)$,

asymptotes: $y = \pm \dfrac{6}{7}x$

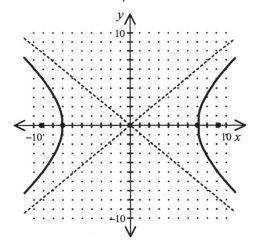

[39]

[9.5.2.40]  *Dynamic Item*

$$\frac{y^2}{9} - \frac{x^2}{16} = 1$$

vertices: $(0, 3)$, $(0, -3)$; foci: $(0, 5)$, $(0, -5)$;

asymptotes: $y = \frac{3}{4}x$, $y = -\frac{3}{4}x$

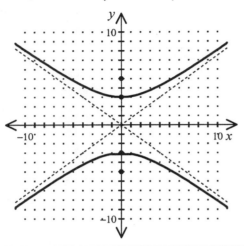

[40] _____

**Lesson 6: Solving Nonlinear Systems**

Objective 1: Solve a system of equations involving first- or second-degree equations in two variables.

[9.6.1.41]  *Dynamic Item*

[41]  [D]

[9.6.1.42]  *Dynamic Item*

[42]  [C]

[9.6.1.43]  *Dynamic Item*

[43]  two solutions: $(0, 3)$ and $(3, 0)$

[9.6.1.44]  *Dynamic Item*

[44]  four solutions: $\left(\pm 8\sqrt{2}, \pm 4\right)$

Objective 2:  Identify a conic section from its equation.

[9.6.2.45]  *Dynamic Item*

[45]  [A]

[9.6.2.46]  *Dynamic Item*

[46]  [B]

[9.6.2.47]  *Dynamic Item*

[47]  $(x+1)^2 + (y+1)^2 = 1$; circle

[9.6.2.48]  *Dynamic Item*

[48]  $\dfrac{(x+4)^2}{4} - \dfrac{(y-5)^2}{2} = 1$; hyperbola

**Lesson 1: Introduction to Probability**

Objective 1: Find the theoretical probability of an event.

[10.1.1.1] *Dynamic Item*

1. Teesha is in the chess club. There are 21 students in the club. Two of them will be picked at random to attend an awards banquet. What is the probability that Teesha will *not* be randomly chosen to attend the banquet?

   [A] $\dfrac{19}{21}$      [B] $\dfrac{21}{19}$      [C] $\dfrac{21}{2}$      [D] $\dfrac{2}{21}$

[10.1.1.2] *Dynamic Item*

2. A spinner is evenly divided into 8 equal areas and numbered from 1 through 8. What is the probability of spinning a number less than 4 in a single spin?

   [A] $\dfrac{1}{4}$      [B] $\dfrac{1}{2}$      [C] $\dfrac{5}{8}$      [D] $\dfrac{3}{8}$

[10.1.1.3] *Dynamic Item*

3. A box contains 4 green, 5 yellow, and 3 purple balls. Find the probability of obtaining a yellow ball in a single random draw.

[10.1.1.4] *Dynamic Item*

4. Determine the probability that you will roll the number 2 on a number cube.

**Lesson 1: Introduction to Probability**

Objective 2: Apply the Fundamental Counting Principle.

[10.1.2.5] *Dynamic Item*

5. Janelle went to the mall to buy a shirt for a friend. Her choices for shirt style are henley and corduroy. Both of the choices come in blue, purple, and green. Draw a tree diagram that represents her choices.

[A]

corduroy
henley
blue
purple
green

[B]

blue
purple
green

[C]

corduroy
blue
purple
green

henley
blue
purple
green

[D]

corduroy
henley

[10.1.2.6] *Dynamic Item*

6. A lunch menu consists of 6 different kinds of sandwiches, 2 different kinds of soup, and 6 different drinks. How many choices are there for ordering a sandwich, a bowl of soup, and a drink?

[A] 14        [B] 72        [C] 1,036,800        [D] 3

**Lesson 1:  Introduction to Probability**

[10.1.2.7]  *Dynamic Item*

7.  A cafe serves a variety of stuffed potatoes. You can choose from russet, yellow, or white potatoes with any one of 9 different fillings. How many different varieties of stuffed potatoes can you choose from?

[10.1.2.8]  *Dynamic Item*

8.  At a pizza parlor, Isabel has a choice of pizza toppings and sizes. There are topping choices of hamburger, pepperoni, and sausage and size choices of giant and mini. Draw a tree diagram that shows the number of possible single-topping pizzas of either size that Isabel can order.

**Lesson 2:  Permutations**

Objective 1:  Solve problems involving linear permutations of distinct or indistinguishable objects.

[10.2.1.9]  *Dynamic Item*

9.  How many different arrangements can be made using all of the letters in the word GRAPHICS?

    [A] 28                  [B] 208                  [C] 8                  [D] 40,320

[10.2.1.10]  *Dynamic Item*

10. Find: $_6P_3$       [A] 9         [B] 18         [C] 120         [D] 240

[10.2.1.11]  *Dynamic Item*

11. If no two letters are repeated, and if the letters do not have to form a word, how many different 4-letter combinations can be made from the letters m, n, o, p, q, r?

[10.2.1.12]  *Dynamic Item*

12. How many different ways can 7 different runners finish in first, second, and third places in a race?

**Lesson 2: Permutations**

Objective 2: Solve problems involving circular permutations.

[10.2.2.13] *Dynamic Item*

13. A circular, rotating, serving tray has 8 different desserts placed around its circumference. How many different ways can all of the desserts be arranged on the circular tray?

    [A] 40,320          [B] 5040          [C] 3,628,800          [D] 362,880

[10.2.2.14] *Dynamic Item*

14. How many different ways can 6 people be seated around a circular table?

    [A] 120          [B] 60          [C] 720          [D] 30

[10.2.2.15] *Dynamic Item*

15. How many ways can 6 keys be arranged on a circular key ring? Remember, a key ring can be turned over.

[10.2.2.16] *Dynamic Item*

16. Cleopatra and 8 of her advisors sat around a circular table. How many seating arrangements were possible?

**Lesson 3: Combinations**

Objective 1: Solve problems involving combinations.

[10.3.1.17] *Dynamic Item*

17. Evaluate: $_7C_4$          [A] 840          [B] 35          [C] 56          [D] 2

[10.3.1.18] *Dynamic Item*

18. Four cards are drawn in succession and without replacement from a standard deck of 52 cards. How many sets of four cards are possible?

    [A] 1,082,900          [B] 270,725          [C] 6,497,400          [D] 54,145

**Lesson 3: Combinations**

[10.3.1.19] *Dynamic Item*

19. Mario, Bob, Neil, Leila, Jane, and Jack are in the math club. The club advisor will assign students to 4-person teams at the next Math Team competition. How many different 4-person teams can be formed from these six students?

[10.3.1.20] *Dynamic Item*

20. Evaluate: $\dfrac{_{14}C_4 \times _{17}C_{11}}{_{16}C_6}$

Objective 2: Solve problems by distinguishing between permutations and combinations.

[10.3.2.21] *Dynamic Item*

21. How many distinct committees of 10 people can be formed if the people are drawn from a pool of 18 people? Use factorials to express the answer.

[A] $_{18}C_9 = \dfrac{18!}{8!\ 9!}$    [B] $_{18}C_{10} = \dfrac{18!}{7!\ 10!}$    [C] $_{18}C_{10} = \dfrac{18!}{8!\ 10!}$    [D] $_{18}C_{11} = \dfrac{18!}{7!\ 11!}$

[10.3.2.22] *Dynamic Item*

22. A hat contains 25 names, 14 of which are female. If eight names are randomly drawn from the hat, what is the probability that at least four male names are drawn?

[A] 0.199    [B] 0.496    [C] 0.801    [D] 0.504

[10.3.2.23] *Dynamic Item*

23. How many different dogsled teams of 6 dogs can be formed if the dogs are chosen from a group of 15 dogs? Use factorials to express your answer.

[10.3.2.24] *Dynamic Item*

24. A state lottery consists of drawing 6 numbers from the first 36 positive integers. Find the probability of winning the lottery.

**Lesson 4: Using Addition With Probability**

Objective 1: Find the probabilities of mutually exclusive events.

[10.4.1.25] *Dynamic Item*

25. Suppose you mix-up the cards below and choose one without looking. What is the probability of selecting "D" or "M"?

| M | K | J | D | T | L | L |

[A] 1      [B] $\frac{2}{7}$      [C] $\frac{5}{7}$      [D] $\frac{2}{5}$

[10.4.1.26] *Dynamic Item*

26. If the number cards below were shuffled and a card were drawn at random, what is the probability of drawing an 8 or a 7?

| 8 | 8 | 3 | 7 | 1 | 3 | 3 | 4 |

[A] $\frac{1}{2}$      [B] $\frac{3}{8}$      [C] $\frac{1}{8}$      [D] $\frac{1}{32}$

[10.4.1.27] *Dynamic Item*

27. A spinner is numbered from 1 through 8 with each number equally likely to occur. What is the probability of obtaining a number less than 3 or greater than 6 with a single spin?

[10.4.1.28] *Dynamic Item*

28. Suppose two fair dice are rolled. What is the probability that a sum of 2 or 3 turns up?

**Lesson 4:  Using Addition With Probability**

Objective 2:  Find the probabilities of inclusive events.

[10.4.2.29]  *Dynamic Item*

29.  Two cards are randomly selected from a standard 52-card deck. What is the probability of getting 2 clubs or 2 face cards?

[A]  0.106  [B]  0.098  [C]  0.094  [D]  0.090

[10.4.2.30]  *Dynamic Item*

30.  If all possible results are equally likely, find the probability that a spin of the spinner below would land on a capital letter or a consonant.

[A]  $\dfrac{3}{10}$  [B]  $\dfrac{9}{10}$  [C]  $\dfrac{7}{10}$  [D]  $\dfrac{4}{5}$

[10.4.2.31]  *Dynamic Item*

31.  Two cards are randomly selected from a standard 52-card deck. What is the probability of getting 2 hearts or 2 numbers less than 4 (count aces as 1)? Note: A result of 1 heart and 1 number less than 4 is *not* a favorable outcome.

**Lesson 4:  Using Addition With Probability**

[10.4.2.32]  *Dynamic Item*

32.  If all possible results are equally likely, find the probability of spinning a number that is even or a multiple of 3 using the spinner below.

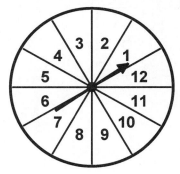

**Lesson 5:  Independent Events**

Objective 1:  Find the probability of two or more independent events.

[10.5.1.33]  *Dynamic Item*

33.  A coin is tossed and a number cube is rolled. What is the probability that the coin shows tails and the die shows  a 3 or a 4?

[A] $\dfrac{1}{6}$          [B] $\dfrac{1}{12}$          [C] $\dfrac{5}{6}$          [D] $\dfrac{1}{4}$

[10.5.1.34]  *Dynamic Item*

34.  If 2 blocks are randomly taken from a bag containing 7 blue blocks, 6 red blocks, and 8 yellow blocks, what is the probability of drawing a blue block and a red block?

[A] $\dfrac{1}{10}$          [B] $\dfrac{2}{13}$          [C] $\dfrac{21}{200}$          [D] $\dfrac{7}{26}$

**Lesson 5: Independent Events**

[10.5.1.35] *Dynamic Item*

35. What is the probability of randomly drawing a card with the number 3 on it and the spinner landing on the number 8? Assume that the spinner is divided equally.

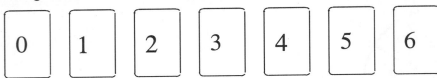

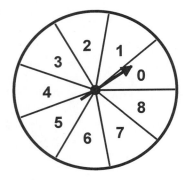

[10.5.1.36] *Dynamic Item*

36. Two urns each contain black balls and red balls. The first urn contains 3 black balls and 5 red balls and the second urn contains 3 black balls and 2 red balls. A ball is drawn randomly from each urn. What is the probability that both balls are red?

**Lesson 6: Dependant Events and Conditional Probability**

Objective 1: Find conditional probabilities.

[10.6.1.37] *Dynamic Item*

37. In a bag there are 4 green jelly beans, 3 black jelly beans, and 7 yellow jelly beans. Once a jelly bean is drawn, it is not replaced. Find the probability of randomly drawing a green jelly bean and then a black jelly bean in two consecutive draws.

[A] $\dfrac{1}{26}$ [B] $\dfrac{1}{13}$ [C] $\dfrac{3}{49}$ [D] $\dfrac{6}{91}$

**Lesson 6:  Dependant Events and Conditional Probability**

[10.6.1.38]  *Dynamic Item*

38.  Two cards are randomly drawn in succession from a deck of 52 playing cards. Find the probability that any jack and any queen are drawn, in that order, without replacement.

[A]  $\dfrac{1}{663}$           [B]  $\dfrac{1}{221}$           [C]  $\dfrac{4}{663}$           [D]  $\dfrac{1}{2652}$

[10.6.1.39]  *Dynamic Item*

39.  On-The-Go Car Rentals has a total of 60 rental cars, including twenty-two 4-door cars and twenty-six cars with 4-wheel drive. Six of the 4-door cars come equipped with 4-wheel drive. One customer (who didn't care what type of car she drove) asked for any car chosen at random. Find the probability that the car chosen for her has 4-wheel drive if it is known that the car does not have four doors.

[10.6.1.40]  *Dynamic Item*

40.  Each person in a group of students was identified by his or her hair color and then asked whether he or she preferred taking classes in the morning, afternoon, or evening. The results are shown in the table below. Find the probability that a randomly selected student in this group is a brunette given that he or she preferred afternoon classes.

| Preference | Blonde | Brunette | Redhead |
|------------|--------|----------|---------|
| Morning    | 20     | 25       | 10      |
| Afternoon  | 35     | 50       | 5       |
| Evening    | 40     | 30       | 45      |

**Lesson 7: Experimental Probability and Simulation**

Objective 1: Use simulation methods to estimate or approximate the experimental probability of an event.

[10.7.1.41]  *Dynamic Item*

41. Evan and Iris tossed a coin 40 times and got heads 19 times. What is the experimental probability of tossing a head using Evan and Iris's results?

   [A] $\dfrac{21}{59}$    [B] $\dfrac{19}{59}$    [C] $\dfrac{21}{40}$    [D] $\dfrac{19}{40}$

[10.7.1.42]  *Dynamic Item*

42. Jamila spins a spinner with 7 sections of equal area, like the one below, 40 times. It lands on the 3 five times. What is the experimental probability of spinning a 3?

   [A] $\dfrac{1}{8}$    [B] $\dfrac{1}{7}$    [C] $\dfrac{3}{5}$    [D] $\dfrac{3}{40}$

**Lesson 7:  Experimental Probability and Simulation**

[10.7.1.43]  *Dynamic Item*

43.  The table shows the batting records for members of a softball team.

| Player | Number of hits | Times at bat |
|--------|---------------|--------------|
| Sherise | 10 | 16 |
| Lena | 6 | 10 |
| Su | 15 | 22 |
| Juanita | 18 | 24 |

a. Find the observed probability that Juanita gets a hit.
b. Find the observed probability that Su does not get a hit.


[10.7.1.44]  *Dynamic Item*

44.  In your last 25 soccer games, you attempted 125 goals and made 50. What is the experimental probability that you will make a goal in your next attempt? Write your answer as a decimal.

**Lesson 1: Introduction to Probability**

Objective 1: Find the theoretical probability of an event.

[10.1.1.1] *Dynamic Item*

[1]  [A]

[10.1.1.2] *Dynamic Item*

[2]  [D]

[10.1.1.3] *Dynamic Item*

[3]  $\dfrac{5}{12}$

[10.1.1.4] *Dynamic Item*

[4]  $\dfrac{1}{6}$

Objective 2: Apply the Fundamental Counting Principle.

[10.1.2.5] *Dynamic Item*

[5]  [C]

[10.1.2.6] *Dynamic Item*

[6]  [B]

[10.1.2.7] *Dynamic Item*

[7]  27

[10.1.2.8] *Dynamic Item*

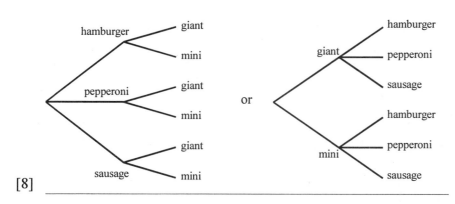

[8] _____

**Lesson 2: Permutations**

Objective 1: Solve problems involving linear permutations of distinct or indistinguishable objects.

[10.2.1.9] *Dynamic Item*

[9]  [D]_____

[10.2.1.10] *Dynamic Item*

[10]  [C]_____

[10.2.1.11] *Dynamic Item*

[11]  360 _____

[10.2.1.12] *Dynamic Item*

[12]  $_7P_3 = 210$ _____

Objective 2: Solve problems involving circular permutations.

[10.2.2.13] *Dynamic Item*

[13]  [B]_____

[10.2.2.14] *Dynamic Item*

[14] [A]

[10.2.2.15] *Dynamic Item*

[15] 60

[10.2.2.16] *Dynamic Item*

[16] 5040

### Lesson 3: Combinations

Objective 1: Solve problems involving combinations.

[10.3.1.17] *Dynamic Item*

[17] [B]

[10.3.1.18] *Dynamic Item*

[18] [B]

[10.3.1.19] *Dynamic Item*

[19] 15

[10.3.1.20] *Dynamic Item*

[20] 1547

Objective 2: Solve problems by distinguishing between permutations and combinations.

[10.3.2.21] *Dynamic Item*

[21] [C]

[10.3.2.22]  *Dynamic Item*

[22]  [D]

[10.3.2.23]  *Dynamic Item*

[23]  $_{15}C_6 = \dfrac{15!}{9!\,6!}$

[10.3.2.24]  *Dynamic Item*

[24]  $\dfrac{6! \times 30!}{36!} = \dfrac{1}{1{,}947{,}792}$

## Lesson 4: Using Addition With Probability

Objective 1: Find the probabilities of mutually exclusive events.

[10.4.1.25]  *Dynamic Item*

[25]  [B]

[10.4.1.26]  *Dynamic Item*

[26]  [B]

[10.4.1.27]  *Dynamic Item*

[27]  $\dfrac{1}{2}$

[10.4.1.28]  *Dynamic Item*

[28]  $\dfrac{1}{12}$

Objective 2: Find the probabilities of inclusive events.

[10.4.2.29] *Dynamic Item*

[29]  [A]

[10.4.2.30] *Dynamic Item*

[30]  [B]

[10.4.2.31] *Dynamic Item*

[31]  $\dfrac{_{13}C_2 + {}_{12}C_2 - {}_3C_2}{_{52}C_2} \approx 0.106$

[10.4.2.32] *Dynamic Item*

[32]  $\dfrac{2}{3}$

**Lesson 5:  Independent Events**

Objective 1: Find the probability of two or more independent events.

[10.5.1.33] *Dynamic Item*

[33]  [A]

[10.5.1.34] *Dynamic Item*

[34]  [A]

[10.5.1.35] *Dynamic Item*

[35]  $\dfrac{1}{63}$

[10.5.1.36] *Dynamic Item*

[36] $\dfrac{1}{4}$

**Lesson 6: Dependant Events and Conditional Probability**

Objective 1: Find conditional probabilities.

[10.6.1.37] *Dynamic Item*

[37] [D]

[10.6.1.38] *Dynamic Item*

[38] [C]

[10.6.1.39] *Dynamic Item*

[39] $\dfrac{10}{19}$

[10.6.1.40] *Dynamic Item*

[40] $\dfrac{5}{9}$

**Lesson 7: Experimental Probability and Simulation**

Objective 1: Use simulation methods to estimate or approximate the experimental probability of an event.

[10.7.1.41] *Dynamic Item*

[41] [D]

[10.7.1.42] *Dynamic Item*

[42] [A]

[10.7.1.43]  *Dynamic Item*

    a. $\dfrac{3}{4}$

[43]   b. $\dfrac{7}{22}$
_____

[10.7.1.44]  *Dynamic Item*

[44]  0.4
_____

**Lesson 1: Sequences and Series**

Objective 1: Find the terms of a sequence.

[11.1.1.1] *Dynamic Item*

1. Write the next two terms in the sequence 2, 6, 10, 14, . . .

   [A] 19, 23          [B] 17, 21          [C] 26, 30          [D] 18, 22

[11.1.1.2] *Dynamic Item*

2. Write the first five terms of the sequence defined by the given recursive or explicit formula.
   $t_1 = 2,\ t_2 = 3$
   $t_{n+2} = -3t_{n+1} + 3t_n$

   [A] 2, 3, –15, 36, –63          [B] 2, 3, –9, 27, –81

   [C] 2, 3, 15, 54, 207          [D] 2, 3, –3, 18, –63

[11.1.1.3] *Dynamic Item*

3. Write the first five terms of the sequence defined by the given recursive or explicit formula.
   $t_n = 43 - 6n$

[11.1.1.4] *Dynamic Item*

4. Write the first five terms of the sequence defined by the given recursive or explicit formula.
   $t_n = \dfrac{n(n-4)}{4}$

Objective 2: Evaluate the sum of a series expressed in sigma notation.

[11.1.2.5] *Dynamic Item*

5. Evaluate the sum: $\sum_{k=4}^{8}(2k+1)$          [A] 35          [B] 65          [C] 56          [D] 80

**Lesson 1:  Sequences and Series**

[11.1.2.6]  *Dynamic Item*

6.  Write the terms of the series. Then evaluate the sum.

$$\sum_{k=0}^{4}(2k+2)$$

[A]  $2 + 4 + 6 + 8$; 30

[B]  $2 + 4 + 6 + 8 + 10$; 20

[C]  $2 + 4 + 6 + 8$; 20

[D]  $2 + 4 + 6 + 8 + 10$; 30

[11.1.2.7]  *Dynamic Item*

7.  Write the terms of the series. Then evaluate the sum.

$$\sum_{n=1}^{7} 2\left(-\frac{1}{2}\right)^{n-1}$$

[11.1.2.8]  *Dynamic Item*

8.  Evaluate the sum:  $\sum_{k=4}^{8}\left(k^2 + 2k + 2\right)$

**Lesson 2:  Arithmetic Sequences**

Objective 1:  Recognize arithmetic sequences, and find the indicated term of an arithmetic sequence.

[11.2.1.9]  *Dynamic Item*

9.  The average cost of an automobile in the U.S. in 1990 was $22,954. Since then, average increases have occurred at a rate of $1380 yearly. Write the general term for the arithmetic sequence modeling automobile costs, where $n = 1$ corresponds to 1990.

[A]  $t_n = 22,954 + 1380n$

[B]  $t_n = 21,574 + 1380n$

[C]  $t_n = 22,954 - 21,574n$

[D]  $t_n = 1380 + 22,954n$

**Lesson 2: Arithmetic Sequences**

[11.2.1.10] *Dynamic Item*

10. Use the given formula to find the first four terms of the arithmetic sequence.
$t_n = 59 - 9n$

[A] 41, 32, 23, 14          [B] 50, 41, 32, 23

[C] 50, 59, 68, 77          [D] 50, –450, 4050, –36,450

[11.2.1.11] *Dynamic Item*

11. Use the given formula to find the first five terms of the arithmetic sequence.
$t_n = 36 - 4n$

[11.2.1.12] *Dynamic Item*

12. State whether $\dfrac{1}{2}, \dfrac{1}{4}, \dfrac{1}{8}, \dfrac{1}{16}, \dfrac{1}{32}$ is an arithmetic sequence. If it is, identify the common difference, $d$.

Objective 2: Find arithmetic means between two numbers.

[11.2.2.13] *Dynamic Item*

13. Find the three arithmetic means between 4 and –4.

[A] 2, 0, –2      [B] 5, 2, –1      [C] –2, –4, –6      [D] 2, 6, 10

[11.2.2.14] *Dynamic Item*

14. Find the four arithmetic means between –7 and 113.

[A] 17, 41, 65, 89    [B] 17, 10, 3, –4    [C] 24, 48, 72, 96    [D] 20, 43, 66, 89

[11.2.2.15] *Dynamic Item*

15. Find the five arithmetic means between 3 and –39.

**Lesson 2: Arithmetic Sequences**

[11.2.2.16] *Dynamic Item*

16. Find the six arithmetic means between 3 and −18.

**Lesson 3: Arithmetic Series**

Objective 1: Find the sum of the first $n$ terms of an arithmetic series.

[11.3.1.17] *Dynamic Item*

17. A 30-row theater has 40 seats in the front row. The second row has 41 seats. If each row has one more than the row in front of it, how many seats are there in the theater?

    [A] 3270          [B] 3300          [C] 1635          [D] 1650

[11.3.1.18] *Dynamic Item*

18. Evaluate the sum.          [A] 1200          [B] 1008          [C] 108          [D] 1056

$$\sum_{k=1}^{24}(4k-8)$$

[11.3.1.19] *Dynamic Item*

19. Evaluate the sum.

$$\sum_{k=1}^{12}(-2k-3)$$

[11.3.1.20] *Dynamic Item*

20. Find the sum of the first 12 terms of the sequence 3, 7, 11, 15, ...

**Lesson 4:  Geometric Sequences**

Objective 1:  Recognize geometric sequences, and find the indicated term of a geometric sequence.

[11.4.1.21]  *Dynamic Item*

21.  Write the first five terms of the geometric sequence using the given explicit formula.

$$t_n = 10 \cdot \left(\frac{1}{5}\right)^n$$

[A]  $2, \dfrac{2}{5}, \dfrac{2}{25}, \dfrac{2}{125}, \dfrac{2}{625}$

[B]  $10, 2, \dfrac{2}{5}, \dfrac{2}{25}, \dfrac{2}{125}$

[C]  $10, \dfrac{11}{5}, \dfrac{6}{5}, \dfrac{13}{15}, \dfrac{7}{10}$

[D]  $10, 2, \dfrac{5}{3}, \dfrac{10}{7}, \dfrac{5}{4}$

[11.4.1.22]  *Dynamic Item*

22.  Write an explicit formula for the *n*th term of the geometric sequence.
  5 , 10 , 20 , 40, ...

[A]  $t_n = 5 \cdot (2)^{n-1}$     [B]  $t_n = 5 \cdot (2)^{n+1}$     [C]  $t_n = 5 \cdot (3)^{n-1}$     [D]  $t_n = \dfrac{2}{5} \cdot (3)^n$

[11.4.1.23]  *Dynamic Item*

23.  Write an explicit formula for the *n*th term of the geometric sequence.
  $\dfrac{1}{2}, \ -\dfrac{1}{4}, \ \dfrac{1}{6}, \ -\dfrac{1}{8}, \ \cdots$

[11.4.1.24]  *Dynamic Item*

24.  State whether the following is a geometric sequence. If it is, identify the common ratio, *r*.
  $\dfrac{1}{2}, \ \dfrac{1}{2}, \ \dfrac{1}{2}, \ \dfrac{1}{2}, \ \dfrac{1}{2}$

**Lesson 4: Geometric Sequences**

Objective 2: Find the geometric means between two numbers.

[11.4.2.25] *Dynamic Item*

25. Find the two geometric means between 2 and 432.

    [A] 12, 24         [B] 12, 72         [C] 10, 50         [D] 14, 98

[11.4.2.26] *Dynamic Item*

26. Find the three *positive* geometric means between 6 and $\dfrac{3}{8}$.

    [A] $3, \dfrac{3}{2}, \dfrac{3}{4}$     [B] $\dfrac{12}{5}, \dfrac{24}{25}, \dfrac{48}{125}$   [C] $\dfrac{3}{2}, \dfrac{3}{8}, \dfrac{3}{32}$   [D] $\dfrac{9}{2}, \dfrac{27}{8}, \dfrac{81}{32}$

[11.4.2.27] *Dynamic Item*

27. Find the four geometric means between 4 and –31,104.

[11.4.2.28] *Dynamic Item*

28. Find three geometric means between 11 and $\dfrac{2816}{81}$ for both a *positive* and a *negative* value of $r$.

**Lesson 5: Geometric Series and Mathematical Induction**

Objective 1: Find the sum of the first $n$ terms of a geometric series.

[11.5.1.29] *Dynamic Item*

29. Find the sum of the geometric series $0.1 + 0.01 + 0.001 + \ldots$ given the formula $S = \dfrac{a}{1-r}$, where $a$ is the first term, $r$ is the common ratio, and $S$ is the sum.

    [A] 0.111         [B] 0.003         [C] $\dfrac{1}{9}$         [D] $\dfrac{1}{10}$

**Lesson 5: Geometric Series and Mathematical Induction**

[11.5.1.30] *Dynamic Item*

30. Find the sum of the first 6 terms of the geometric series $8 + \dfrac{8}{3} + \dfrac{8}{9} + \dfrac{8}{27} + \ldots$

   [A] 11.87         [B] 11.98         [C] 21.93         [D] 48

[11.5.1.31] *Dynamic Item*

31. Find the sum of the geometric series $(0.994) + (0.994)^2 + (0.994)^3 + \ldots$ given the formula $S = \dfrac{a}{1-r}$, where $a$ is the first term, $r$ is the common ratio, and $S$ is the sum.

[11.5.1.32] *Dynamic Item*

32. Find the sum of the first 7 terms of the geometric series $6 + 8 + \dfrac{32}{3} + \dfrac{128}{9} + \dfrac{512}{27} + \ldots$

   Give the answers to the nearest hundredth, if necessary.

**Objective 2:** Use mathematical induction to prove statements about natural numbers.

[11.5.2.33] *Dynamic Item*

33. Let $P(n)$ represent the statement:
$5 + 13 + 21 + \ldots + (8n - 3) = 4n^2 + 1n$
In the proof that $P(n)$ is true for all integers $n$, $n \geq 1$, what term must be added to both sides of $P(k)$ to show $P(k+1)$ follows from $P(k)$?

   [A] $8k + 5$         [B] $8k - 3$         [C] $P(k + 1)$         [D] $8k + 13$

**Lesson 5: Geometric Series and Mathematical Induction**

[11.5.2.34] *Dynamic Item*

34. Make a conjecture about the pattern of the given data. Find the sum of the 8th row.
$$2$$
$$2 + 4 + 2$$
$$2 + 4 + 6 + 4 + 2$$
$$2 + 4 + \ldots + (2n-2) + (2n) + (2n-2) + \ldots + 2$$

    [A] The sums of the rows are 2, 8, 18, . . . . The sum of the $n$th row is $n(n+3)$. The sum of the 8th row is 88.

    [B] The sums of the rows are 2, 6, 12, . . . . The sum of the $n$th row is $n^2 + n$. The sum of the 8th row is 72.

    [C] The sums of the rows are 2, 8, 18, . . . . The sum of the $n$th row is $2n^2$. The sum of the 8th row is 128.

    [D] The sums of the rows are 2, 8, 18, . . . . The sum of the $n$th row is $(n+1)^2 - (n-1)$. The sum of the 8th row is 74.

[11.5.2.35] *Dynamic Item*

35. Let $P(n)$ represent the statement:
$$6 + 14 + 22 + \cdots + (8n-2) = 4n^2 + 2n$$
Use the principle of mathematical induction to show that $P(n)$ is true for all integers $n$, $n \geq 1$.

[11.5.2.36] *Dynamic Item*

36. Let $P(n)$ represent the statement:
$$2 + 6 + 10 + \ldots + (4n - 2) = 2n^2$$
In the proof that $P(n)$ is true for all integers $n$, $n \geq 1$, what term must be added to both sides of $P(k)$ to show $P(k+1)$ follows from $P(k)$?

**Lesson 6: Infinite Series**

Objective 1: Find the sum of an infinite geometric series, if one exists.

[11.6.1.37] *Dynamic Item*

37. Find the sum of the infinite geometric series, if it exists.

$$-4 + \frac{8}{3} - \frac{16}{9} + \frac{32}{27} - \frac{64}{81} + \ldots$$

[A] $-\dfrac{12}{7}$      [B] $\dfrac{8}{3}$      [C] $-\dfrac{8}{5}$      [D] $-\dfrac{12}{5}$

[11.6.1.38] *Dynamic Item*

38. Find the sum of the infinite geometric series, if it exists.

$$\sum_{k=1}^{\infty} -4(4)^{k-1}.$$

[A] 0      [B] −16      [C] 4      [D] none

[11.6.1.39] *Dynamic Item*

39. Find the sum of the infinite geometric series, if it exists.

$$3 - \frac{9}{2} + \frac{27}{4} - \frac{81}{8} + \frac{243}{16} - \ldots$$

[11.6.1.40] *Dynamic Item*

40. Find the sum of the infinite geometric series, if it exists.

$$\sum_{k=1}^{\infty} 4\left(-\frac{4}{5}\right)^{k-1}.$$

Objective 2: Write repeating decimals as fractions.

[11.6.2.41] *Dynamic Item*

41. Write $0.4\overline{6}$ as a fraction in $\dfrac{a}{b}$ form.      [A] $\dfrac{7}{11}$   [B] $\dfrac{7}{15}$   [C] $\dfrac{1}{2}$   [D] $\dfrac{3}{7}$

### Lesson 6: Infinite Series

[11.6.2.42] *Dynamic Item*

42. Express $0.23\overline{84}$ as a geometric series, and write its sum as the ratio of two integers.

[A] $\dfrac{23}{100} + \sum\limits_{n=1}^{\infty} \dfrac{21}{2500}\left(\dfrac{1}{100}\right)^{n} = \dfrac{787}{3300}$

[B] $\dfrac{23}{100} + \sum\limits_{n=1}^{\infty} \dfrac{21}{2500}\left(\dfrac{1}{100}\right)^{n} = \dfrac{359}{1650}$

[C] $\dfrac{23}{100} + \sum\limits_{n=0}^{\infty} \dfrac{21}{2500}\left(\dfrac{1}{100}\right)^{n} = \dfrac{787}{3300}$

[D] $\dfrac{23}{100} + \sum\limits_{n=1}^{\infty} \dfrac{21}{2500}\left(\dfrac{1}{100}\right)^{n-1} = \dfrac{359}{1650}$

[11.6.2.43] *Dynamic Item*

43. Write $0.\overline{63}$ as the ratio of two integers.

[11.6.2.44] *Dynamic Item*

44. Express $0.47\overline{18}$ as a geometric series, and write its sum as the ratio of two integers.

### Lesson 7: Pascal's Triangle

Objective 1: Find entries in Pascal's triangle.

[11.7.1.45] *Dynamic Item*

45. Find the 4th and 8th entries in the row 12 of Pascal's triangle.

    [A] 220; 792        [B] 78; 1716        [C] 55; 462        [D] 66; 924

[11.7.1.46] *Dynamic Item*

46. Use Pascal's triangle to solve for the value of $n$: $3\left({}_{n}C_{6}\right) = {}_{n+1}C_{6}$

    [A] 6        [B] 8        [C] 11        [D] 7

[11.7.1.47] *Dynamic Item*

47. Find the 3rd and 6th entries in the row 12 of Pascal's triangle.

**Lesson 7: Pascal's Triangle**

[11.7.1.48]  *Dynamic Item*

48.  Use Pascal's triangle to solve for the value of $n$: $2(_nC_1) = {_{n+1}}C_2$

Objective 2:  Use Pascal's triangle to find combinations and probabilities.

[11.7.2.49]  *Dynamic Item*

49.  Use Pascal's triangle to find the number of ways to choose 2 boxes from 5 boxes.

    [A] 5         [B] 6         [C] 15         [D] none of these

[11.7.2.50]  *Dynamic Item*

50.  Use Pascal's Triangle to determine the probability that you will get three red lights in a row of five lights. Assume red and green are equally likely occurrences.

    [A] $\dfrac{5}{16}$         [B] $\dfrac{1}{32}$         [C] $\dfrac{3}{16}$         [D] $\dfrac{5}{32}$

[11.7.2.51]  *Dynamic Item*

51.  Use Pascal's Triangle to determine the probability of getting two heads when tossing a coin four times.

[11.7.2.52]  *Dynamic Item*

52.  Use Pascal's triangle to find the number of ways to choose 3 boxes from 7 boxes.

**Lesson 8: The Binomial Theorem**

Objective 1: Use the Binomial Theorem to expand $(x+y)^2$.

[11.8.1.53] *Dynamic Item*

53. Expand the binomial raised to a power.

$(a-2b)^4$

[A] $a^4 - 8a^3b + 12a^2b^2 - 8ab^3 + 16b^4$  [B] $a^4 + 8a^3b + 24a^2b^2 + 32ab^3 + 16b^4$

[C] $a^4 + 8a^3b + 12a^2b^2 + 8ab^3 + 16b^4$  [D] $a^4 - 8a^3b + 24a^2b^2 - 32ab^3 + 16b^4$

[11.8.1.54] *Dynamic Item*

54. Expand the binomial raised to a power.

$(2a-b)^4$

[A] $16a^4 - 8a^3b + 12a^2b^2 - 8ab^3 + b^4$  [B] $16a^4 + 32a^3b + 24a^2b^2 + 8ab^3 + b^4$

[C] $16a^4 + 8a^3b + 12a^2b^2 + 8ab^3 + b^4$  [D] $16a^4 - 32a^3b + 24a^2b^2 - 8ab^3 + b^4$

[11.8.1.55] *Dynamic Item*

55. Expand the binomial raised to a power.

$(2a-b)^4$

[11.8.1.56] *Dynamic Item*

56. Expand the binomial raised to a power.

$(x+y)^6$

Objective 2: Use the Binomial Theorem to calculate a probability.

[11.8.2.57] *Dynamic Item*

57. A bowler usually gets 12 strikes for every 30 balls she bowls. What is the probability that she will get exactly 6 strikes with her next 10 balls?

[A] $\approx 0.13$   [B] $\approx 0.111$   [C] $\approx 0.86$   [D] $\approx 0.004$

**Lesson 8:  The Binomial Theorem**

[11.8.2.58]  *Dynamic Item*

58.  There are 9 cars in a parking lot on a very cold day. Suppose the probability of any one of them not starting is 0.15. What is the probability that exactly 2 of the cars will not start?

   [A]  $\approx 0.321$          [B]  $\approx 0.81$          [C]  $\approx 0.26$          [D]  $\approx 0.023$

[11.8.2.59]  *Dynamic Item*

59.  A fair coin is tossed 13 times. What is the probability of obtaining exactly 11 heads? Express the answer both in terms of $_nC_k$ and as a four-place decimal.

[11.8.2.60]  *Dynamic Item*

60.  A basbeball pitcher's batting average is 0.130. What is the probability that the pitcher will get exactly 2 hits during 12 at bats?

**Lesson 1: Sequences and Series**

Objective 1: Find the terms of a sequence.

[11.1.1.1] *Dynamic Item*

[1]  [D]

[11.1.1.2] *Dynamic Item*

[2]  [D]

[11.1.1.3] *Dynamic Item*

[3]  37, 31, 25, 19, 13

[11.1.1.4] *Dynamic Item*

[4]  $-\dfrac{3}{4},\ -1,\ -\dfrac{3}{4},\ 0,\ \dfrac{5}{4}$

Objective 2: Evaluate the sum of a series expressed in sigma notation.

[11.1.2.5] *Dynamic Item*

[5]  [B]

[11.1.2.6] *Dynamic Item*

[6]  [D]

[11.1.2.7] *Dynamic Item*

[7]  $2 - 1 + \dfrac{1}{2} - \dfrac{1}{4} + \dfrac{1}{8} - \dfrac{1}{16} + \dfrac{1}{32};\ \dfrac{43}{32}$

[11.1.2.8] *Dynamic Item*

[8]  260

**Algebra 2**

**Lesson 2: Arithmetic Sequences**

Objective 1: Recognize arithmetic sequences, and find the indicated term of an arithmetic sequence.

[11.2.1.9]  *Dynamic Item*

 [9]  [B]

 [11.2.1.10]  *Dynamic Item*

[10]  [B]

 [11.2.1.11]  *Dynamic Item*

[11]  32, 28, 24, 20, 16

 [11.2.1.12]  *Dynamic Item*

[12]  no

Objective 2: Find arithmetic means between two numbers.

 [11.2.2.13]  *Dynamic Item*

[13]  [A]

 [11.2.2.14]  *Dynamic Item*

[14]  [A]

 [11.2.2.15]  *Dynamic Item*

[15]  −4, −11, −18, −25, −32

 [11.2.2.16]  *Dynamic Item*

[16]  0, −3, −6, −9, −12, −15

**Lesson 3: Arithmetic Series**

Objective 1: Find the sum of the first $n$ terms of an arithmetic series.

[11.3.1.17] *Dynamic Item*

[17]  [C]

[11.3.1.18] *Dynamic Item*

[18]  [B]

[11.3.1.19] *Dynamic Item*

[19]  −192

[11.3.1.20] *Dynamic Item*

[20]  300

**Lesson 4: Geometric Sequences**

Objective 1: Recognize geometric sequences, and find the indicated term of a geometric sequence.

[11.4.1.21] *Dynamic Item*

[21]  [A]

[11.4.1.22] *Dynamic Item*

[22]  [A]

[11.4.1.23] *Dynamic Item*

[23]  $t_n = \dfrac{(-1)^{n+1}}{2n}$

[11.4.1.24] *Dynamic Item*

[24]   yes, $r = 1$

Objective 2: Find the geometric means between two numbers.

[11.4.2.25] *Dynamic Item*

[25]   [B]

[11.4.2.26] *Dynamic Item*

[26]   [A]

[11.4.2.27] *Dynamic Item*

[27]   $-24, 144, -864, 5184$

[11.4.2.28] *Dynamic Item*

[28]   $\dfrac{44}{3}, \dfrac{176}{9}, \dfrac{704}{27}$ and $-\dfrac{44}{3}, \dfrac{176}{9}, -\dfrac{704}{27}$

**Lesson 5: Geometric Series and Mathematical Induction**

Objective 1: Find the sum of the first $n$ terms of a geometric series.

[11.5.1.29] *Dynamic Item*

[29]   [C]

[11.5.1.30] *Dynamic Item*

[30]   [B]

[11.5.1.31] *Dynamic Item*

[31]   165.667

[11.5.1.32]  *Dynamic Item*

[32]  116.85

Objective 2:  Use mathematical induction to prove statements about natural numbers.

[11.5.2.33]  *Dynamic Item*

[33]  [A]

[11.5.2.34]  *Dynamic Item*

[34]  [C]

[11.5.2.35]  *Dynamic Item*

(I)  $n = 1$: $8 \cdot 1 - 2 = 6$ and $4 \cdot 1^2 + 2 \cdot 1 = 6$

(II) If $6 + 14 + 22 + \cdots + (8k - 2) = 4k^2 + 2k$,

then $6 + 14 + 22 + \cdots + (8k - 2) + 8(k + 1) - 2 = 4k^2 + 2k + 8(k + 1) - 2$

$= 4k^2 + 10k + 6$

$= 4k^2 + 8k + 4 + 2k + 2$

$= 4(k^2 + 2k + 1) + 2k + 2$

[35]  $= 4(k + 1)^2 + 2(k + 1)$

[11.5.2.36]  *Dynamic Item*

[36]  $4k + 2$

**Lesson 6:  Infinite Series**

Objective 1:  Find the sum of an infinite geometric series, if one exists.

[11.6.1.37]  *Dynamic Item*

[37]  [D]

[11.6.1.38] *Dynamic Item*

[38] [D]

[11.6.1.39] *Dynamic Item*

[39] none

[11.6.1.40] *Dynamic Item*

[40] $\dfrac{20}{9}$

Objective 2: Write repeating decimals as fractions.

[11.6.2.41] *Dynamic Item*

[41] [B]

[11.6.2.42] *Dynamic Item*

[42] [C]

[11.6.2.43] *Dynamic Item*

[43] $\dfrac{7}{11}$

[11.6.2.44] *Dynamic Item*

[44] $\dfrac{47}{100} + \sum_{n=0}^{\infty}\dfrac{9}{5000}\left(\dfrac{1}{100}\right)^{n} = \dfrac{519}{1100}$

**Lesson 7: Pascal's Triangle**

Objective 1: Find entries in Pascal's triangle.

[11.7.1.45] *Dynamic Item*

[45]  [A]

[11.7.1.46] *Dynamic Item*

[46]  [B]

[11.7.1.47] *Dynamic Item*

[47]  66; 792

[11.7.1.48] *Dynamic Item*

[48]  3

Objective 2: Use Pascal's triangle to find combinations and probabilities.

[11.7.2.49] *Dynamic Item*

[49]  [D]

[11.7.2.50] *Dynamic Item*

[50]  [A]

[11.7.2.51] *Dynamic Item*

[51]  $\dfrac{3}{8}$

[11.7.2.52] *Dynamic Item*

[52]  35

**Lesson 8: The Binomial Theorem**

Objective 1: Use the Binomial Theorem to expand $(x+y)^2$.

[11.8.1.53]  *Dynamic Item*

[53]  [D]

[11.8.1.54]  *Dynamic Item*

[54]  [D]

[11.8.1.55]  *Dynamic Item*

[55]  $16a^4 - 32a^3b + 24a^2b^2 - 8ab^3 + b^4$

[11.8.1.56]  *Dynamic Item*

[56]  $x^6 + 6x^5y + 15x^4y^2 + 20x^3y^3 + 15x^2y^4 + 6xy^5 + y^6$

Objective 2: Use the Binomial Theorem to calculate a probability.

[11.8.2.57]  *Dynamic Item*

[57]  [B]

[11.8.2.58]  *Dynamic Item*

[58]  [C]

[11.8.2.59]  *Dynamic Item*

[59]  $_{13}C_2(0.5)^{13} \approx 0.0095$

[11.8.2.60]  *Dynamic Item*

[60]  $\approx 0.277$

**Lesson 1:  Measures of Central Tendency**

Objective 1:  Find the mean, median, and mode of a data set.

[12.1.1.1]  *Dynamic Item*

1.  Find the mean, the median, and mode of the data set: 19, 4, 23, 21, 17, 26, 29, 6, 17

    [A]  $\bar{x} = 18$; 19; 17     [B]  $\bar{x} = 19$; 18; 19     [C]  $\bar{x} = 18$; 19; 19     [D]  $\bar{x} = 19$; 18; 17

[12.1.1.2]  *Dynamic Item*

2.  The depth of snow at seven different mountain lodges is 15 in., 18 in., 24 in., 19 in., 87 in., 15 in., and 21 in. Find the mean, median, and mode. Tell which measure is the most useful for predicting how deep the snow will be at an eighth lodge.

    [A]  $\bar{x} = 28.4$ in.;  19 in.;  15 in.          [B]  $\bar{x} = 19$ in.;  28.4 in.;  15 in.
        The mean is the most useful.                   The median is the most useful.

    [C]  $\bar{x} = 28.4$ in.;  19 in.;  15 in.          [D]  $\bar{x} = 19$ in.;  28.4 in.;  15 in.
        The median is the most useful.                 The mean is the most useful.

[12.1.1.3]  *Dynamic Item*

3.  The number of patients treated in a dental office each day was recorded for 10 days.  Find the mean, median, and mode for this set of numbers.
    5, 30, 20, 28, 16, 28, 28, 12, 10, 28

[12.1.1.4]  *Dynamic Item*

4.  Terry recorded the weights of the first ten fish he caught and then released at Hag Lake this season. The weights were 6 lb, 3 lb, 8 lb, 3 lb, 4 lb, 2 lb, 5 lb, 3 lb, 20 lb, and 3 lb. Terry wants to know what weight of fish he caught the most often. Find the mean, median, and mode. Tell which measure is most useful for Terry.

**Lesson 1: Measures of Central Tendency**

Objective 2: Find or estimate the mean from a frequency table of data.

[12.1.2.5] *Dynamic Item*

5. A mail-order catalog offers 33 items for sale at the following prices: five items for $18, eight items for $21, thirteen items for $25, and seven items for $32. Prepare a frequency table showing the number of items offered at each price. Then use the table to find the average price for all 33 catalog items.

[A]

| Price | Number of Items | Product ($×No.) |
|-------|-----------------|-----------------|
| $18   | 5               | $90             |
| $21   | 8               | $168            |
| $25   | 13              | $325            |
| $32   | 7               | $224            |

average price = $24.45

[B]

| Price | Number of Items | Product ($×No.) |
|-------|-----------------|-----------------|
| $32   | 5               | $160            |
| $25   | 8               | $200            |
| $21   | 13              | $273            |
| $18   | 7               | $126            |

average price = $23.00

[C]

| Price | Number of Items | Product ($×No.) |
|-------|-----------------|-----------------|
| $32   | 5               | $160            |
| $25   | 8               | $200            |
| $21   | 13              | $273            |
| $18   | 7               | $126            |

average price = $24.94

[D]

| Price | Number of Items | Product ($×No.) |
|-------|-----------------|-----------------|
| $18   | 5               | $90             |
| $21   | 8               | $168            |
| $25   | 13              | $325            |
| $32   | 7               | $224            |

average price = $24.00

**Lesson 1: Measures of Central Tendency**

[12.1.2.6] *Dynamic Item*

6. The students in an algebra class took their final exam, and the results are given in the frequency table below. Which completed frequency table used the average of each score interval times the number of students in that interval for the values in the product column, and then used the results to estimate the average student score for the entire class of 22 students?

| Score Interval | Students | Product |
|---|---|---|
| 50–59 | 5 | |
| 60–69 | 4 | |
| 70–79 | 7 | |
| 80–89 | 5 | |
| 90–100 | 1 | |

[A]

| Score Interval | Students | Product |
|---|---|---|
| 50–59 | 5 | 250 |
| 60–69 | 4 | 240 |
| 70–79 | 7 | 490 |
| 80–89 | 5 | 400 |
| 90–100 | 1 | 90 |

average score ≈ 66.82

[B]

| Score Interval | Students | Product |
|---|---|---|
| 50–59 | 5 | 272.5 |
| 60–69 | 4 | 258 |
| 70–79 | 7 | 521.5 |
| 80–89 | 5 | 422.5 |
| 90–100 | 1 | 95 |

average score ≈ 71.34

[C]

| Score Interval | Students | Product |
|---|---|---|
| 50–59 | 5 | 397.5 |
| 60–69 | 4 | 378 |
| 70–79 | 7 | 766.5 |
| 80–89 | 5 | 622.5 |
| 90–100 | 1 | 140 |

average score = 104.75

[D]

| Score Interval | Students | Product |
|---|---|---|
| 50–59 | 5 | 275 |
| 60–69 | 4 | 260 |
| 70–79 | 7 | 525 |
| 80–89 | 5 | 425 |
| 90–100 | 1 | 95 |

average score ≈ 71.82

**Lesson 1:  Measures of Central Tendency**

[12.1.2.7]  *Dynamic Item*

7.  Use the frequency table below, with the a total of 15 catalog items sold at four different prices, to find the average price per item.

| Price | Number of Items | Price × Items = Product |
|-------|-----------------|-------------------------|
| $11   | 4               | $44                     |
| $14   | 2               | $28                     |
| $17   | 3               | $51                     |
| $20   | 6               | $120                    |

[12.1.2.8]  *Dynamic Item*

8.  An algebra class was taken by 26 students. Their final scores were: four As, four Bs, seven Cs, six Ds, and five Fs. Prepare a frequency table to represent the students' final algebra grades. Then use the table to find the mean grade point score, using A = 4, for the entire group of  26 students. Give the answer to the nearest hundredth, if necessary.

**Lesson 2:  Stem-and-Leaf Plots, Histograms, and Circle Graphs**

Objective 1:  Make a stem-and-leaf plot, a histogram, or a circle graph for a data set.

[12.2.1.9]  *Dynamic Item*

9.  Listed below is the percentage of students registered for various majors at college. Use this information to make a circle graph.

| Business    | 25% | Liberal Arts | 30% |
|-------------|-----|--------------|-----|
| Engineering | 15% | Undecided    | 30% |

## Lesson 2: Stem-and-Leaf Plots, Histograms, and Circle Graphs

[A]

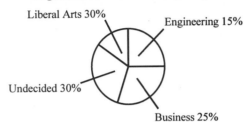

**Registration of Various College Majors**

[B]

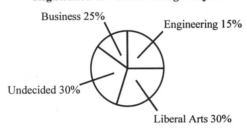

**Registration of Various College Majors**

[C]

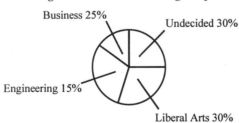

**Registration of Various College Majors**

**Lesson 2: Stem-and-Leaf Plots, Histograms, and Circle Graphs**

[D]

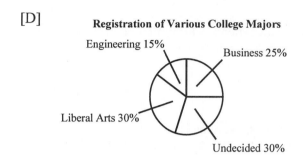

**Registration of Various College Majors**

[12.2.1.10] *Dynamic Item*

10. The golf scores for the 26 members of the Belmont Country Club were 74, 92, 119, 103, 85, 107, 86, 118, 91, 78, 73, 96, 105, 89, 101, 92, 84, 97, 104, 87, 88, 101, 95, 103, 99, 92. Which histogram correctly shows the frequency distribution of the scores using ten-point intervals?

[A]

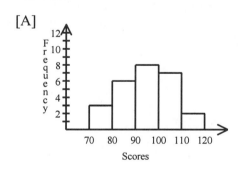

[B]

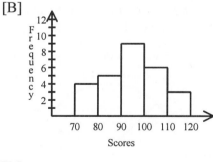

[C]

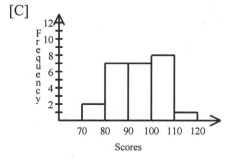

[D]

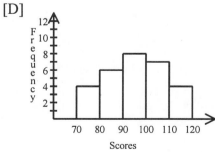

**Lesson 2: Stem-and-Leaf Plots, Histograms, and Circle Graphs**

[12.2.1.11]  *Dynamic Item*

11.  Make a stem-and-leaf plot for the following data. Then find the median and the mode.
     6.2, 8.1, 6.5, 8.6, 7.7, 9.7, 7.1, 8.6, 7.9, 6.3, 8.4, 7.3, 6.8, 9.9, 6.4

[12.2.1.12]  *Dynamic Item*

12.  Test scores for the 20 members of the algebra class were as follows:
     76, 98, 67, 59, 82, 83, 61, 54, 75, 59, 73, 68, 87, 81, 75, 62, 76, 64, 73, 77
     Create a relative frequency histogram using ten-point intervals to show the distribution of
     the scores.

Objective 2:  Find and use relative frequencies to solve probability problems.

[12.2.2.13]  *Dynamic Item*

13.  In Sean's school there are 144 families which have 4 children. The circle graph shows the
     probability of each combination of girls and boys in a family with four children. Use the
     circle graph to predict the probability that one of these 144 families, chosen at random, will
     have at least one child of each sex.

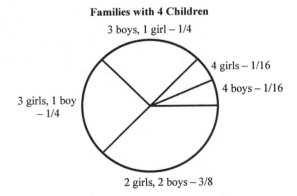

**Families with 4 Children**
3 boys, 1 girl – 1/4
4 girls – 1/16
4 boys – 1/16
3 girls, 1 boy – 1/4
2 girls, 2 boys – 3/8

[A] 62.5%          [B] 87.5%          [C] 37.5%          [D] 50%

**Lesson 2: Stem-and-Leaf Plots, Histograms, and Circle Graphs**

[12.2.2.14] *Dynamic Item*

14. The relative frequency histogram below represents the age in years of the first 100 children to have their portraits taken at the "See What Develops" photography studio. What is the probability that the next child to have portraits taken will be between 1 and 2 years old?

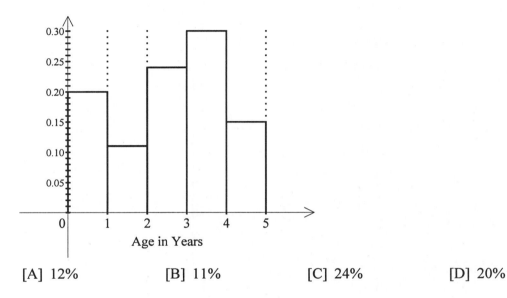

[A] 12%     [B] 11%     [C] 24%     [D] 20%

[12.2.2.15] *Dynamic Item*

15. The following stem-and-leaf plot shows the basketball scores for the Wolves for the first 24 games of their regular season.

| Basketball Scores for the Wolves | |
|---|---|
| Stem | Leaf |
| 5 | 4 6 9 9 9 |
| 6 | 2 3 5 5 7 |
| 7 | 0 1 2 5 5 7 7 8 |
| 8 | 0 3 3 4 7 9 |

Use the plot to predict the probability that the Wolves will score 70-79 points in their next game. Round the probability to the nearest tenth of a percent.

**Lesson 2: Stem-and-Leaf Plots, Histograms, and Circle Graphs**

[12.2.2.16] *Dynamic Item*

16. Use the histogram to determine the probability that a student chosen at random from Harmon Middle School will be 65-67 inches tall. Round the probability to the nearest tenth of a percent.

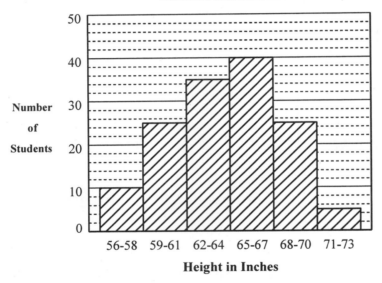

**Heights of Students at**

**Harmon Middle School**

**Lesson 3: Box-and-Whisker Plots**

Objective 1: Find the range, quartiles, and inter-quartile range for a data set.

[12.3.1.17] *Dynamic Item*

17. Find the minimum and maximum values, quartiles, range, and interquartile range for the data set.
14, 6, 11, 47, 13, 12, 20, 30, 3, 49, 36

[A] minimum $= 3$; $Q_1 = 11$; $Q_2 = 14$; $Q_3 = 36$;
maximum $= 49$; range $= 46$; IQR $= 25$

[B] minimum $= 3$; $Q_1 = 6$; $Q_2 = 13$; $Q_3 = 30$;
maximum $= 49$; range $= 46$; IQR $= 24$

[C] minimum $= 3$; $Q_1 = 12$; $Q_2 = 20$; $Q_3 = 47$;
maximum $= 49$; range $= 46$; IQR $= 35$

[D] minimum $= 3$; $Q_1 = 9$; $Q_2 = 22$; $Q_3 = 36$;
maximum $= 49$; range $= 46$; IQR $= 27$

[12.3.1.18] *Dynamic Item*

18. Find the minimum and maximum values, quartiles, range, and interquartile range for the data set.
33, 18, 35, 15, 19, 42, 25, 32, 24, 34, 3, 5

[A] minimum $= 3$; $Q_1 = 18$; $Q_2 = 24.5$; $Q_3 = 33$;
maximim $= 42$; range $= 39$; IQR $= 15$

[B] minimum $= 3$; $Q_1 = 16.5$; $Q_2 = 24$; $Q_3 = 33.5$;
maximim $= 42$; range $= 39$; IQR $= 17$

[C] minimum $= 3$; $Q_1 = 15$; $Q_2 = 24$; $Q_3 = 34$;
maximim $= 42$; range $= 39$; IQR $= 19$

[D] minimum $= 3$; $Q_1 = 16.5$; $Q_2 = 24.5$; $Q_3 = 33.5$;
maximim $= 42$; range $= 39$; IQR $= 17$

**Lesson 3: Box-and-Whisker Plots**

[12.3.1.19]  *Dynamic Item*

19. Find the minimum and maximum values, quartiles, range, and interquartile range for the data set.
    7.8, 5, 7.3, 3.8, 6.2, 4.4, 1.7, 4.3, 7.2, 8.4, 2.7, 2.6

[12.3.1.20]  *Dynamic Item*

20. Find the minimum and maximum values, quartiles, range, and interquartile range for the data set.
    143, 377, 266, 164, 363, 255, 272, 340, 117, 373, 124

Objective 2:  Make a box-and-whisker plot for a data set.

[12.3.2.21]  *Dynamic Item*

21. Find the minimum and maximum values, $Q_1$, $Q_2$, and $Q_3$ for the following data. Then use these values to draw a box-and-whisker plot.
    30, 18, 18, 21, 22, 32, 24, 24, 23, 28, 31, 26, 29, 26, 20

[A]  minimum = 17; maximum = 32;
$Q_1 = 20$; $Q_2 = 25$; $Q_3 = 29$

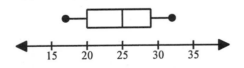

[B]  minimum = 18; maximum = 32;
$Q_1 = 21$; $Q_2 = 24$; $Q_3 = 29$

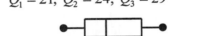
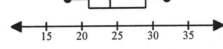

[C]  minimum = 18; maximum = 34;
$Q_1 = 21$; $Q_2 = 25$; $Q_3 = 29$

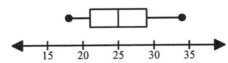

[D]  minimum = 18; maximum = 33;
$Q_1 = 21$; $Q_2 = 24$; $Q_3 = 30$

**Lesson 3: Box-and-Whisker Plots**

[12.3.2.22] *Dynamic Item*

22. Find the minimum and maximum values, $Q_1$, $Q_2$, and $Q_3$ for the following data. Then use these values to draw a box-and-whisker plot.
   5.2, 6.2, 3.2, 2.2, 7.2, 6.2, 6.2, 3.2, 3.2, 6.2, 2.2, 3.2, 5.2, 3.2, 7.2

[A]　minimum $= 2.1$; maximum $= 7.2$;
$Q_1 = 3.1$; $Q_2 = 4.7$; $Q_3 = 6.2$

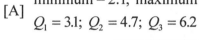
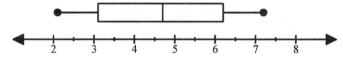

[B]　minimum $= 2.2$; maximum $= 7.4$;
$Q_1 = 3.2$; $Q_2 = 4.7$; $Q_3 = 6.2$

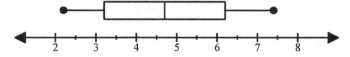

[C]　minimum $= 2.2$; maximum $= 7.2$;
$Q_1 = 3.2$; $Q_2 = 5.2$; $Q_3 = 6.2$

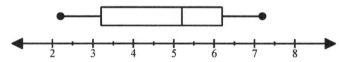

[D]　minimum $= 2.2$; maximum $= 7.3$;
$Q_1 = 3.2$; $Q_2 = 5.2$; $Q_3 = 6.3$

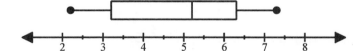

**Lesson 3: Box-and-Whisker Plots**

[12.3.2.23] *Dynamic Item*

23. Find the minimum and maximum values, $Q_1$, $Q_2$, and $Q_3$ for the following data. Then use these values to draw a box-and-whisker plot.
    40, 41, 46, 32, 30, 42, 43, 33, 28, 30, 24, 45, 25, 51, 51

[12.3.2.24] *Dynamic Item*

24. Find the minimum and maximum values, $Q_1$, $Q_2$, and $Q_3$ for the following data. Then use these values to draw a box-and-whisker plot.
    122, 125, 138, 122, 109, 107, 106, 129, 107, 132, 123, 102, 127, 117, 127

**Lesson 4: Measures of Dispersion**

Objective 1: Calculate and use measures of dispersion, such as range, mean deviation, variance, and standard deviation.

[12.4.1.25] *Dynamic Item*

25. Find the variance and the standard deviation for the following data.
    7, 18, 11, 15, 19, 5, 21, 16, 14

    [A] variance $= 27$; standard deviation $\approx 5.20$

    [B] variance $= 26$; standard deviation $\approx 5.10$

    [C] variance $= 26$; standard deviation $\approx 5.20$

    [D] variance $= 27$; standard deviation $\approx 5.10$

[12.4.1.26] *Dynamic Item*

26. A number cube is tossed 10 times with these results: 1, 1, 3, 5, 3, 6, 4, 6, 2, 4
    Find the range and mean deviation of the data.

    [A] range $= 6$
    mean deviation $= 1.5$

    [B] range $= 5$
    mean deviation $= 1.7$

    [C] range $= 5$
    mean deviation $= 1.5$

    [D] range $= 6$
    mean deviation $= 1.7$

**Lesson 4:  Measures of Dispersion**

[12.4.1.27]  *Dynamic Item*

27.  A number cube is tossed 10 times with the following results.
2, 6, 2, 2, 3, 5, 5, 1, 5, 4
Find the range and the mean deviation of the data.


[12.4.1.28]  *Dynamic Item*

28.  A number cube is tossed 10 times with the following results.
6, 6, 3, 1, 4, 1, 4, 1, 6, 3
Find the mean deviation, the variance, and the standard deviation of the data


**Lesson 5:  Binomial Distributions**

Objective 1:  Find the probability of $r$ successes in $n$ trials of a binomial experiment.

[12.5.1.29]  *Dynamic Item*

29.  A company guarantees customer satisfaction on the purchase of a product, or the company
will refund the purchase price of the product. Previous experience has shown that 8% of all
purchases are returned. What is the probability that no more than 1 of the next 7 purchases
will be returned?

  [A]  $\approx 0.011$        [B]  $\approx 0.103$        [C]  $\approx 0.989$        [D]  $\approx 0.897$


[12.5.1.30]  *Dynamic Item*

30.  A biologist is collecting insects in a field. Beetles represent 55 percent of all the insects that
have been collected so far. What is the probability that at least half of the next 8 insects
collected will be beetles?

  [A]  0.260381        [B]  0.254        [C]  0.739619        [D]  0.751

**Lesson 5: Binomial Distributions**

[12.5.1.31] *Dynamic Item*

31. A company guarantees customer satisfaction on the purchase of a product, or the company will refund the purchase price of the product. Previous experience has shown that 10% of the purchases are returned. What is the probability that no more than 1 of the next 6 purchases will be returned?

[12.5.1.32] *Dynamic Item*

32. A number cube is tossed 14 times. What is the probability of obtaining exactly 3 fours? Give the answer as a four-place decimal.

**Lesson 6: Normal Distributions**

Objective 1: Find the probability of an event given that the data is normally distributed and its mean and standard deviation are known.

[12.6.1.33] *Dynamic Item*

33. The personal savings of the Young Saver Club were normally distributed with a mean of $625 and a standard deviation of $90. What is the probability that a randomly selected saver has an account total between $715 and $805?

   [A] 0.6826        [B] 0.0215        [C] 0.1359        [D] 0.3413

[12.6.1.34] *Dynamic Item*

34. The heights of all the 11-year-old boys in the United States are normally distributed with a mean of 57 inches and a standard deviation of 2.5 inches. What is the probability that a boy chosen at random from that age group will have a height less than 64.5 inches?

   [A] 99.87%        [B] 49.87%        [C] 97.72%        [D] 0.13%

**Lesson 6: Normal Distributions**

[12.6.1.35] *Dynamic Item*

35. Last year, the personal best high jumps of track athletes in a nearby state were normally distributed with a mean of 228 cm and a standard deviation of 20 cm. What is the probability that a randomly selected high jumper has a personal best between 228 and 248 cm?

[12.6.1.36] *Dynamic Item*

36. The life expectancy (in hours) of a fluorescent tube is normally distributed with a mean 7000 and a standard deviation 1000. Find the probability that a tube lasts for more than 8050 hours.

Objective 2: Use $z$-scores to find probabilities.

[12.6.2.37] *Dynamic Item*

37. In a certain normal distribution of scores, the mean is 60 and the standard deviation is 8. Find the $z$-score corresponding to a score of 67 and find the percentage of the scores that are below 67.

   [A] 0.44; 87.29%     [B] 1.09; 86.21%     [C] 0.88; 81.06%     [D] 1.14; 67.00%

[12.6.2.38] *Dynamic Item*

38. The class average on a math test was 81.5 and the standard deviation was 5.8. Find the $z$-score for a test score of 91, and the percentage of the class who scored below 91.

   [A] $\approx -0.16$; 43.64%          [B] $\approx 0.16$; 56.36%

   [C] $\approx 1.64$; 94.95%          [D] $\approx -1.64$; 5.05%

[12.6.2.39] *Dynamic Item*

39. In a certain normal distribution of scores, the mean is 30 and the standard deviation is 4. Find the $z$-score corresponding to a score of 32. What percentage of scores were below 32?

**Lesson 6: Normal Distributions**

[12.6.2.40]  *Dynamic Item*

40. The bowling scores of all of the bowlers in 12 bowling leagues are normally distributed. Their mean score is 181 points, with a standard deviation of 22 points. If one league has 160 bowlers, how many of them are likely to score more than 225 points?

**Lesson 1: Measures of Central Tendency**

Objective 1: Find the mean, median, and mode of a data set.

[12.1.1.1] *Dynamic Item*

[1]  [A]

[12.1.1.2] *Dynamic Item*

[2]  [C]

[12.1.1.3] *Dynamic Item*

[3]  $\bar{x} = 20.5$;  24;  28

[12.1.1.4] *Dynamic Item*

   $\bar{x} = 5.7$;  3.5;  3
[4]  The mode is the most useful.

Objective 2: Find or estimate the mean from a frequency table of data.

[12.1.2.5] *Dynamic Item*

[5]  [A]

[12.1.2.6] *Dynamic Item*

[6]  [B]

[12.1.2.7] *Dynamic Item*

[7]  $16.20

[12.1.2.8]  *Dynamic Item*

| Grade | Points | Students | Product |
|-------|--------|----------|---------|
| A     | 4      | 4        | 16      |
| B     | 3      | 4        | 12      |
| C     | 2      | 7        | 14      |
| D     | 1      | 6        | 6       |
| F     | 0      | 5        | 0       |

[8]   mean ≈ 1.85

## Lesson 2:  Stem-and-Leaf Plots, Histograms, and Circle Graphs

Objective 1:  Make a stem-and-leaf plot, a histogram, or a circle graph for a data set.

[12.2.1.9]  *Dynamic Item*

[9]  [D]

[12.2.1.10]  *Dynamic Item*

[10]  [A]

[12.2.1.11]  *Dynamic Item*

| Stem | Leaf | 6 | 4 = 6.4 |
|------|------|---|---------|
| 6    | 2 3 4 5 8 |
| 7    | 1 3 7 9 |
| 8    | 1 4 6 6 |
| 9    | 7 9 |

mode = 8.6
[11]  median = 7.7

[12.2.1.12]  *Dynamic Item*

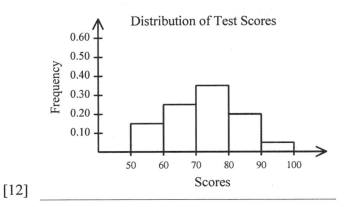

[12]  _____

Objective 2:  Find and use relative frequencies to solve probability problems.

[12.2.2.13]  *Dynamic Item*

[13]  [B]

[12.2.2.14]  *Dynamic Item*

[14]  [B]

[12.2.2.15]  *Dynamic Item*

[15]  33.3% _____

[12.2.2.16]  *Dynamic Item*

[16]  28.6% _____

**Lesson 3: Box-and-Whisker Plots**

Objective 1: Find the range, quartiles, and inter-quartile range for a data set.

[12.3.1.17] *Dynamic Item*

[17]  [A]

[12.3.1.18] *Dynamic Item*

[18]  [D]

[12.3.1.19] *Dynamic Item*

[19]  minimum $= 1.7$; $Q_1 = 3.25$; $Q_2 = 4.7$; $Q_3 = 7.25$; maximum $= 8.4$; range $= 6.7$; IQR $= 4$

[12.3.1.20] *Dynamic Item*

[20]  minimum $= 117$; $Q_1 = 143$; $Q_2 = 266$; $Q_3 = 363$; maximum $= 377$; range $= 260$; IQR $= 220$

Objective 2: Make a box-and-whisker plot for a data set.

[12.3.2.21] *Dynamic Item*

[21]  [B]

[12.3.2.22] *Dynamic Item*

[22]  [C]

[12.3.2.23] *Dynamic Item*

minimum = 24;  maximum = 51;
$Q_1 = 30$;  $Q_2 = 40$;  $Q_3 = 45$

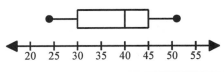

[23] _____

[12.3.2.24] *Dynamic Item*

minimum = 102;  maximum = 138;
$Q_1 = 107$;  $Q_2 = 122$;  $Q_3 = 127$

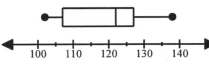

[24] _____

**Lesson 4:  Measures of Dispersion**

Objective 1:  Calculate and use measures of dispersion, such as range, mean deviation, variance, and standard deviation.

[12.4.1.25] *Dynamic Item*

[25]  [B]_____

[12.4.1.26] *Dynamic Item*

[26]  [C]_____

[12.4.1.27] *Dynamic Item*

range = 5
[27]  mean deviation = 1.5 _____

[12.4.1.28]  *Dynamic Item*

    mean deviation $= 1.7$;

    variation $= 3.85$;

[28]  standard deviation $\approx 1.962$

**Lesson 5: Binomial Distributions**

Objective 1: Find the probability of $r$ successes in $n$ trials of a binomial experiment.

[12.5.1.29]  *Dynamic Item*

[29]  [D]

[12.5.1.30]  *Dynamic Item*

[30]  [C]

[12.5.1.31]  *Dynamic Item*

[31]  0.886

[12.5.1.32]  *Dynamic Item*

[32]  0.2268

**Lesson 6: Normal Distributions**

Objective 1: Find the probability of an event given that the data is normally distributed and its mean and standard deviation are known.

[12.6.1.33]  *Dynamic Item*

[33]  [C]

[12.6.1.34]  *Dynamic Item*

[34]  [A]

[12.6.1.35]  *Dynamic Item*

[35]  0.3413

[12.6.1.36]  *Dynamic Item*

[36]  0.1469

Objective 2:  Use *z*-scores to find probabilities.

[12.6.2.37]  *Dynamic Item*

[37]  [C]

[12.6.2.38]  *Dynamic Item*

[38]  [C]

[12.6.2.39]  *Dynamic Item*

[39]  0.50; 69.15%

[12.6.2.40]  *Dynamic Item*

[40]  4

**Lesson 1:  Right-Triangle Trigonometry**

Objective 1:  Find the trigonometric functions of acute angles.

[13.1.1.1]  *Dynamic Item*

1.  Refer to $\triangle ABC$ below to find the indicated value listed. Find the exact value and the value rounded to the nearest ten-thousandth, if necessary.
    Find: cos $x$

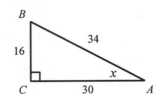

[A]  1 or 1.875　　　[B]  $\dfrac{8}{15}$ or 0.5333　　[C]  $\dfrac{15}{17}$ or 0.8824　　[D]  $\dfrac{8}{17}$ or 0.4706

[13.1.1.2]  *Dynamic Item*

2.  Refer to $\triangle ABC$ below to find the indicated value listed. Find the exact value and the value rounded to the nearest ten-thousandth, if necessary.
    Find: sin $B$

[A]  $\dfrac{3}{5}$ or 0.6　　　　[B]  $\dfrac{5}{3}$ or 1.6667　　[C]  $\dfrac{5}{4}$ or 1.25　　　[D]  $\dfrac{4}{5}$ or 0.8

**Lesson 1: Right-Triangle Trigonometry**

[13.1.1.3]  *Dynamic Item*

3.  Refer to $\triangle ABC$ below to find the indicated value listed. Find the exact value and the value
    rounded to the nearest ten-thousandth, if necessary.
    Find $\sin x$.

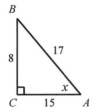

[13.1.1.4]  *Dynamic Item*

4.  Refer to $\triangle ABC$ below to find the indicated value listed. Find the exact value and the value
    rounded to the nearest ten-thousandth, if necessary.
    Find $\tan A$.

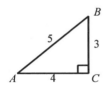

Objective 2:  Solve a right triangle by using trigonometric functions.

[13.1.2.5]  *Dynamic Item*

5.  For $\triangle ABC$, find the measure of $\angle A$ to the nearest degree.

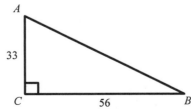

[A]  59°               [B]  69°               [C]  31°               [D]  27°

**Lesson 1: Right-Triangle Trigonometry**

[13.1.2.6] *Dynamic Item*

6. Use the following information to find the unknown sides and angles. $m\angle B = 30°$ ; $c = 12$

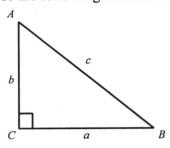

[A] $a = 10.4$; $b = 6$; $m\angle A = 60°$; $m\angle C = 90°$

[B] $a = 11.6$; $b = 6$; $m\angle A = 70°$; $m\angle C = 90°$

[C] $a = 11.6$; $b = 4.5$; $m\angle A = 60°$; $m\angle C = 90°$

[D] $a = 10.4$; $b = 4.5$; $m\angle A = 70°$; $m\angle C = 90°$

[13.1.2.7] *Dynamic Item*

7. Given that $m\angle A = 25°$ and $a = 13$, find the unknown sides and angles.

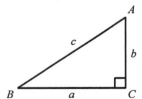

**Lesson 1:  Right-Triangle Trigonometry**

[13.1.2.8]  *Dynamic Item*

8.  For $\triangle ABC$, find the measure of $\angle B$ to the nearest degree.

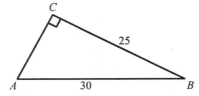

**Lesson 2:  Angles of Rotation**

Objective 1:  Find coterminal and reference angles.

[13.2.1.9]  *Dynamic Item*

9.  Find the reference angle for 194°.      [A]  76°      [B]  166°      [C]  104°      [D]  14°

[13.2.1.10]  *Dynamic Item*

10.  For the angle below, find all coterminal angles $\theta$ such that $-360° < \theta < 360°$. Then find the corresponding reference angle, if it exists.
    207°

    [A]  −163; 17°          [B]  153; 27°          [C]  163; 17°          [D]  −153; 27°

[13.2.1.11]  *Dynamic Item*

11.  For the angle below, find all coterminal angles $\theta$ such that $-360° < \theta < 360°$. Then find the corresponding reference angle, if it exists.
    −72°

[13.2.1.12]  *Dynamic Item*

12.  What is the reference angle for $-526°$ ?

**Lesson 2: Angles of Rotation**

Objective 2: Find the trigonometric function values of angles in standard position.

[13.2.2.13] *Dynamic Item*

13. Find the exact values of the six trigonometric functions of $\theta$ given the point $P(3, 5)$ on the terminal side of $\theta$ in standard position.

[A] $\sin = \dfrac{3\sqrt{34}}{34}$, $\tan = \dfrac{5}{3}$, $\sec = \dfrac{\sqrt{34}}{5}$, $\cos = \dfrac{5\sqrt{34}}{34}$, $\cot = \dfrac{3}{5}$, $\csc = \dfrac{\sqrt{34}}{3}$

[B] $\sin = \dfrac{3\sqrt{34}}{34}$, $\tan = \dfrac{3}{5}$, $\sec = \dfrac{\sqrt{34}}{3}$, $\cos = \dfrac{5\sqrt{34}}{34}$, $\cot = \dfrac{5}{3}$, $\csc = \dfrac{\sqrt{34}}{5}$

[C] $\sin = \dfrac{5\sqrt{34}}{34}$, $\tan = \dfrac{5}{3}$, $\sec = \dfrac{\sqrt{34}}{3}$, $\cos = \dfrac{3\sqrt{34}}{34}$, $\cot = \dfrac{3}{5}$, $\csc = \dfrac{\sqrt{34}}{5}$

[D] $\sin = \dfrac{5}{3}$, $\tan = \dfrac{5\sqrt{34}}{34}$, $\sec = \dfrac{\sqrt{34}}{5}$, $\cos = \dfrac{3}{5}$, $\cot = \dfrac{3\sqrt{34}}{34}$, $\csc = \dfrac{\sqrt{34}}{3}$

[13.2.2.14] *Dynamic Item*

14. Given the quadrant of $\theta$ in standard position and a trigonometric function value of $\theta$, find exact values for the remaining functions.

Quadrant II, $\sin\theta = \dfrac{2}{5}$

[A] $\cos\theta = -\dfrac{\sqrt{21}}{5}$

$\tan\theta = -\dfrac{\sqrt{21}}{2}$; $\cot\theta = -\dfrac{2\sqrt{21}}{21}$

$\sec\theta = -\dfrac{5}{2}$; $\csc\theta = \dfrac{5\sqrt{21}}{21}$

[B] $\cos\theta = -\dfrac{5\sqrt{21}}{21}$

$\tan\theta = -\dfrac{\sqrt{21}}{2}$; $\cot\theta = -\dfrac{2\sqrt{21}}{21}$

$\sec\theta = -\dfrac{\sqrt{21}}{5}$; $\csc\theta = -\dfrac{5}{2}$

[C] $\cos\theta = -\dfrac{\sqrt{21}}{5}$

$\tan\theta = -\dfrac{2\sqrt{21}}{21}$; $\cot\theta = -\dfrac{\sqrt{21}}{2}$

$\sec\theta = -\dfrac{5\sqrt{21}}{21}$; $\csc\theta = \dfrac{5}{2}$

[D] $\cos\theta = \dfrac{\sqrt{21}}{5}$

$\tan\theta = -\dfrac{2\sqrt{21}}{21}$; $\cot\theta = -\dfrac{\sqrt{21}}{2}$

$\sec\theta = \dfrac{5}{2}$; $\csc\theta = -\dfrac{5\sqrt{21}}{21}$

**Lesson 2: Angles of Rotation**

[13.2.2.15]  *Dynamic Item*

15. Given the quadrant of $\theta$ in standard position and a trigonometric function value of $\theta$, find exact values for the remaining functions.

Quadrant IV, $\tan \theta = -\dfrac{3}{7}$

[13.2.2.16]  *Dynamic Item*

16. Find the exact values of the six trigonometric functions of $\theta$ given the point $P(3, 7)$ on the terminal side of $\theta$ in standard position.

**Lesson 3: Trigonometric Functions of Any Angle**

Objective 1: Find exact values for trigonometric functions of special angles and their multiples.

[13.3.1.17]  *Dynamic Item*

17. Find the exact value of the sine, cosine, and tangent of $-135°$.

[A] $\sin = \dfrac{\sqrt{2}}{2}$; $\cos = \dfrac{\sqrt{2}}{2}$; $\tan = -1$      [B] $\sin = -\dfrac{\sqrt{2}}{2}$; $\cos = \dfrac{\sqrt{2}}{2}$; $\tan = 1$

[C] $\sin = \dfrac{\sqrt{2}}{2}$; $\cos = -\dfrac{\sqrt{2}}{2}$; $\tan = -1$      [D] $\sin = -\dfrac{\sqrt{2}}{2}$; $\cos = -\dfrac{\sqrt{2}}{2}$; $\tan = 1$

[13.3.1.18]  *Dynamic Item*

18. Point $P$ is located at the intersection of a circle with a radius of $r$ and the terminal side of a angle $\theta$. Find the coordinates of $P$ to the nearest hundredth.
$\theta = 120°$, $r = 5$

[A] $P(-2.5, 4.33)$      [B] $P(-2.7, 3.9)$      [C] $P(-2.68, 4.2)$      [D] $P(2.65, -3.87)$

[13.3.1.19]  *Dynamic Item*

19. Find the exact value of the sine, cosine, and tangent of $1035°$.

**Lesson 3: Trigonometric Functions of Any Angle**

[13.3.1.20] *Dynamic Item*

20. Point $P$ is located at the intersection of a circle with a radius of $r$ and the terminal side of a angle $\theta$. Find the exact coordinates of $P$.
   $\theta = -60°$, $r = 3$

Objective 2: Find approximate values for trigonometric functions of any angle.

[13.3.2.21] *Dynamic Item*

21. Find tan (–323°).  [A] 0.754  [B] 1.327  [C] 0.984  [D] 0.602

[13.3.2.22] *Dynamic Item*

22. Find sec (–317°).  [A] 0.682  [B] 1.367  [C] 1.466  [D] 1.597

[13.3.2.23] *Dynamic Item*

23. Find tan (–327°).

[13.3.2.24] *Dynamic Item*

24. Find sin 413°.

**Lesson 4: Radian Measure and Arc Length**

Objective 1: Convert from degree measure to radian measure and vice versa.

[13.4.1.25] *Dynamic Item*

25. Convert 57° to radians.  [A] $\frac{19}{120}\pi$  [B] $\frac{19}{90}\pi$  [C] $\frac{19}{60}\pi$  [D] $\frac{19}{30}\pi$

[13.4.1.26] *Dynamic Item*

26. Convert $\frac{35}{6}\pi$ to degrees.  [A] 1040°  [B] 2090°  [C] 1050°  [D] 2100°

**Lesson 4:  Radian Measure and Arc Length**

[13.4.1.27]  *Dynamic Item*

27.  Convert $72°$ to radians.

[13.4.1.28]  *Dynamic Item*

28.  Convert $\frac{11}{6}\pi$ to degrees.

Objective 2:  Find arc length.

[13.4.2.29]  *Dynamic Item*

29.  For a circle of radius 7 feet, find the arc length $s$ subtended by a central angle of $\frac{\pi}{3}$ radians. Round to the nearest hundredth.

   [A] 21.99 feet        [B] 1319.47 feet      [C] 14.66 feet        [D] 7.33 feet

[13.4.2.30]  *Dynamic Item*

30.  For a circle of radius 9 feet, find the arc length of a central angle of $6°$.

   [A] $\frac{3}{5}\pi$ feet          [B] $54\pi$ feet          [C] $\frac{3}{10}\pi$ feet          [D] $\frac{9}{10}\pi$ feet

[13.4.2.31]  *Dynamic Item*

31.  For a circle of radius 7 feet, find the arc length $s$ subtended by a central angle of $\frac{\pi}{5}$ radians. Round to the nearest hundredth.

[13.4.2.32]  *Dynamic Item*

32.  Neil watched a bug crawl through an arc of $6°$ along the rim of half a melon. If the radius of the melon was 6 inches, how far did the bug crawl?

**Lesson 5:  Graphing Trigonometric Functions**

Objective 1:  Graph the sine, cosine, and tangent functions and their transformations.

[13.5.1.33]  *Dynamic Item*

33.  Find the amplitude, the period, and the frequency of the graph. Then write an equation for the sine function for the graph.

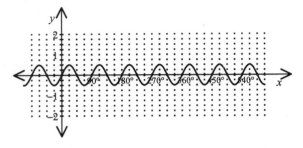

[A]  $1$, $90°$, $\dfrac{1}{4}$, $y = \sin \dfrac{1}{4}x$

[B]  $1$, $45°$, $4$, $y = \sin 4x$

[C]  $\dfrac{1}{2}$, $45°$, $\dfrac{1}{4}$, $y = \dfrac{1}{2}\sin \dfrac{1}{4}x$

[D]  $\dfrac{1}{2}$, $90°$, $4$, $y = \dfrac{1}{2}\sin 4x$

**Lesson 5: Graphing Trigonometric Functions**

[13.5.1.34] *Dynamic Item*

34. Graph: $y = \dfrac{\pi}{4} \tan\left(x + \dfrac{\pi}{4}\right)$

[A]

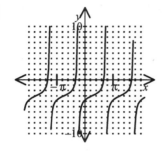

[B]

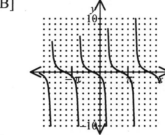

[C]

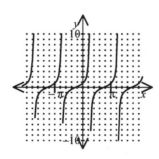

[D] none of these

[13.5.1.35] *Dynamic Item*

35. Sketch the graphs of $y = \sin x$, $y = \sin 2x$, and $y = 2\sin x$. Tell how the graphs are alike and how they are different.

[13.5.1.36] *Dynamic Item*

36. Graph: $y = \dfrac{\pi}{2} \tan\left(x + \dfrac{\pi}{2}\right)$

**Lesson 5: Graphing Trigonometric Functions**

Objective 2: Use the sine function to solve problems.

[13.5.2.37] *Dynamic Item*

37. The function $d = 11 \cos \pi t$ describes a simple harmonic motion, where $d$ is the distance an object travels in $t$ units of time. What is the time required for one complete cycle?

[A] 11           [B] $\dfrac{1}{2}$           [C] 2           [D] $\pi$

[13.5.2.38] *Dynamic Item*

38. The function $d = -2 \cos 6t$ describes a simple harmonic motion, where $d$ is the distance (in meters) an object travels in $t$ seconds. What is the frequency?

[A] 6 cycles/second           [B] 2 cycles/second

[C] $\dfrac{\pi}{3}$ cycles/second           [D] $\dfrac{3}{\pi}$ cycle/second

[13.5.2.39] *Dynamic Item*

39. A block attached to the end of a spring is moving with simple harmonic motion. Its frequency is 60.0 cycles per minute. What is the block's position 8 *seconds* after reaching its maximum amplitude of 13.0 centimeters, and how far will it have travelled during that time?

[13.5.2.40] *Dynamic Item*

40. The function $d = 9 \cos \dfrac{\pi}{3} t$ describes a simple harmonic motion, where $d$ is the distance (in meters) an object travels in $t$ seconds. What is the frequency?

**Lesson 6: Inverses of Trigonometric Functions**

Objective 1: Evaluate trigonometric expressions involving inverses.

[13.6.1.41]  *Dynamic Item*

41.  Evaluate the trigonometric expression.

$$\text{Sin}^{-1}\left(-\frac{1}{2}\right)$$

   [A] 150°          [B] −60°          [C] 120°          [D] −30°

[13.6.1.42]  *Dynamic Item*

42.  Evaluate the trigonometric expression.     [A] $\frac{1}{2}$   [B] $-\frac{\sqrt{2}}{2}$   [C] $-\frac{1}{2}$   [D] $\frac{\sqrt{2}}{2}$

$$\sin\left(\text{Cot}^{-1}-1\right)$$

[13.6.1.43]  *Dynamic Item*

43.  Evaluate the trigonometric expression.

$$\text{Sin}^{-1}\left(-\frac{\sqrt{3}}{2}\right)$$

[13.6.1.44]  *Dynamic Item*

44.  Evaluate the trigonometric expression.

$$\tan\left(\text{Sin}^{-1}\frac{\sqrt{3}}{2}\right)$$

**Lesson 1: Right-Triangle Trigonometry**

Objective 1: Find the trigonometric functions of acute angles.

[13.1.1.1] *Dynamic Item*

[1]  [C]

[13.1.1.2] *Dynamic Item*

[2]  [D]

[13.1.1.3] *Dynamic Item*

[3]  $\dfrac{8}{17}$ or 0.4706

[13.1.1.4] *Dynamic Item*

[4]  $\dfrac{3}{4}$ or 0.75

Objective 2: Solve a right triangle by using trigonometric functions.

[13.1.2.5] *Dynamic Item*

[5]  [A]

[13.1.2.6] *Dynamic Item*

[6]  [A]

[13.1.2.7] *Dynamic Item*

$m\angle B = 65°$

$b \approx 27.88$

[7]  $c \approx 30.76$

[13.1.2.8]  *Dynamic Item*

[8]  34°

**Lesson 2:  Angles of Rotation**

Objective 1:  Find coterminal and reference angles.

[13.2.1.9]  *Dynamic Item*

[9]  [D]

[13.2.1.10]  *Dynamic Item*

[10]  [D]

[13.2.1.11]  *Dynamic Item*

[11]  288° ; 72°

[13.2.1.12]  *Dynamic Item*

[12]  14°

Objective 2:  Find the trigonometric function values of angles in standard position.

[13.2.2.13]  *Dynamic Item*

[13]  [C]

[13.2.2.14]  *Dynamic Item*

[14]  [C]

[13.2.2.15]  *Dynamic Item*

[15]  $\cot = -\dfrac{7}{3}$ ; $\sin = -\dfrac{3\sqrt{58}}{58}$ ; $\cos = \dfrac{7\sqrt{58}}{58}$ ; $\sec = \dfrac{\sqrt{58}}{7}$ ; $\csc = -\dfrac{\sqrt{58}}{3}$

Algebra 2

[13.2.2.16] *Dynamic Item*

[16] $\sin = \dfrac{7\sqrt{58}}{58}$, $\tan = \dfrac{7}{3}$, $\sec = \dfrac{\sqrt{58}}{3}$, $\cos = \dfrac{3\sqrt{58}}{58}$, $\cot = \dfrac{3}{7}$, $\csc = \dfrac{\sqrt{58}}{7}$

**Lesson 3:  Trigonometric Functions of Any Angle**

Objective 1:  Find exact values for trigonometric functions of special angles and their multiples.

[13.3.1.17] *Dynamic Item*

[17]  [D]

[13.3.1.18] *Dynamic Item*

[18]  [A]

[13.3.1.19] *Dynamic Item*

[19]  $-\dfrac{\sqrt{2}}{2}$ ; $\dfrac{\sqrt{2}}{2}$ ; $-1$

[13.3.1.20] *Dynamic Item*

[20]  $P\left(\dfrac{3}{2}, -\dfrac{3\sqrt{3}}{2}\right)$

Objective 2:  Find approximate values for trigonometric functions of any angle.

[13.3.2.21] *Dynamic Item*

[21]  [A]

[13.3.2.22] *Dynamic Item*

[22]  [B]

[13.3.2.23] *Dynamic Item*

[23]  0.649

[13.3.2.24] *Dynamic Item*

[24]  0.799

**Lesson 4:  Radian Measure and Arc Length**

Objective 1:  Convert from degree measure to radian measure and vice versa.

[13.4.1.25] *Dynamic Item*

[25]  [C]

[13.4.1.26] *Dynamic Item*

[26]  [C]

[13.4.1.27] *Dynamic Item*

[27]  $\frac{2}{5}\pi$

[13.4.1.28] *Dynamic Item*

[28]  330°

Objective 2:  Find arc length.

[13.4.2.29] *Dynamic Item*

[29]  [D]

[13.4.2.30] *Dynamic Item*

[30]  [C]

[13.4.2.31] *Dynamic Item*

[31]  4.40 feet

[13.4.2.32] *Dynamic Item*

[32]  0.63 inches

**Lesson 5:  Graphing Trigonometric Functions**

Objective 1:  Graph the sine, cosine, and tangent functions and their transformations.

[13.5.1.33] *Dynamic Item*

[33]  [D]

[13.5.1.34] *Dynamic Item*

[34]  [C]

[13.5.1.35] *Dynamic Item*

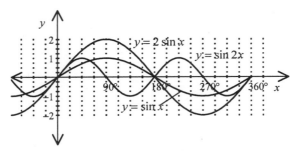

[35]  All three graphs pass through $(0°, 0)$, $(180°, 0)$, and $(360°, 1)$. The graphs of $y = \sin x$ and $y = \sin 2x$ have amplitude 1 while the graph of $y = 2 \sin x$ has amplitude 2. The graphs of $y = \sin x$ and $y = 2 \sin x$ have frequency 1 and period $360°$, while the graph of $y = \sin 2x$ has frequency 2 and period $180°$.

[13.5.1.36]  *Dynamic Item*

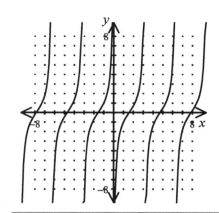

[36] _____

Objective 2:  Use the sine function to solve problems.

[13.5.2.37]  *Dynamic Item*

[37]  [C]

[13.5.2.38]  *Dynamic Item*

[38]  [D]

[13.5.2.39]  *Dynamic Item*

[39]  13.0 cm; 416.0 cm

[13.5.2.40]  *Dynamic Item*

[40]  $\dfrac{1}{6}$ cycle / second

**Lesson 6:  Inverses of Trigonometric Functions**

Objective 1:  Evaluate trigonometric expressions involving inverses.

[13.6.1.41]  *Dynamic Item*

[41]  [D]

[13.6.1.42]  *Dynamic Item*

[42]  [B]

[13.6.1.43]  *Dynamic Item*

[43]  −60°

[13.6.1.44]  *Dynamic Item*

[44]  $\sqrt{3}$

**Lesson 1: The Law of Sines**

Objective 1: Solve mathematical and real-world problems by using the law of sines.

[14.1.1.1] *Dynamic Item*

1. Use the Law of Sines to solve for $m\angle C$ to the nearest tenth.

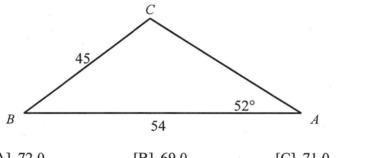

    [A] 72.0          [B] 69.0          [C] 71.0          [D] 70.0

[14.1.1.2] *Dynamic Item*

2. Given a triangle with $a = 11$, $C = 23°$, and $B = 34°$, what is the length of $c$?

    [A] 15.74          [B] 7.69          [C] 5.12          [D] 16.5

[14.1.1.3] *Dynamic Item*

3. Given that $f = 29$, $g = 26$, and $F = 56°$, solve the triangle. If no such triangles exist, write *none*. Round to the nearest tenth.

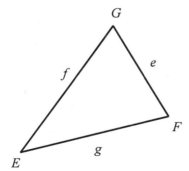

**Lesson 1: The Law of Sines**

[14.1.1.4] *Dynamic Item*

4. Solve this triangle for angle *A*. Then find the area.

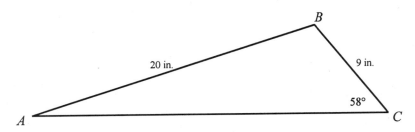

**Lesson 2: The Law of Cosines**

Objective 1: Use the law of cosines to solve triangles.

[14.2.1.5] *Dynamic Item*

5. Solve triangle *ABC* given that $a = 15$, $b = 10$, and $c = 13$.

[A] $A = 80.3°$, $B = 58.7°$, $C = 41.1°$      [B] $A = 80.3°$, $B = 41.1°$, $C = 58.7°$

[C] $A = 41.1°$, $B = 80.3°$, $C = 58.7°$      [D] $A = 58.7°$, $B = 41.1°$, $C = 80.3°$

[14.2.1.6] *Dynamic Item*

6. Use either the Law of Sines or the Law of Cosines to solve for *B* to the nearest tenth.

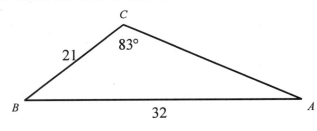

[A] 57.4°      [B] 56.4°      [C] 55.4°      [D] 54.4°

**Lesson 2: The Law of Cosines**

[14.2.1.7] *Dynamic Item*

7. Use the Law of Cosines to solve for $C$ to the nearest tenth of a degree.

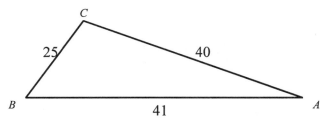

[14.2.1.8] *Dynamic Item*

8. Use either the Law of Sines or the Law of Cosines to solve for $c$ to the nearest tenth.

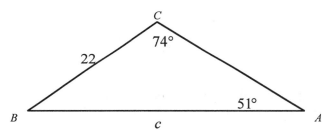

**Lesson 3: Fundamental Trigonometric Identities**

Objective 1: Prove fundamental trigonometric identities.

[14.3.1.9] *Dynamic Item*

9. Which of the following is an identity?

[A] $\dfrac{2\sin^2 x + \cos 2x}{\sec x} = \dfrac{1 - \sin x}{\cos x}$

[B] $\dfrac{2\sin^2 x + \cos 2x}{\sec x} = \dfrac{1 + \sec x}{\sec x}$

[C] $\dfrac{2\sin^2 x + \cos 2x}{\sec x} = \cos x$

[D] $\dfrac{2\sin^2 x + \cos 2x}{\sec x} = \dfrac{1 + \sin x}{\cos x}$

**Lesson 3: Fundamental Trigonometric Identities**

[14.3.1.10] *Dynamic Item*

10. Which of the following possible identities is true?

[A] $\cos 2x - \sin 2x = \tan x$  [B] $\csc 2x - \cot 2x = -\tan x$

[C] $\csc 2x - \cot 2x = \tan x$  [D] $\cos 2x - \sin 2x = -\tan x$

[14.3.1.11] *Dynamic Item*

11. Prove the identity.

$\sin 3x = 3\sin x - 4\sin^3 x$  $\left[\text{Hint: } \sin 3x = \sin(2x + x)\right]$

[14.3.1.12] *Dynamic Item*

12. Prove the identity.

$$\frac{\sec x}{\csc x - \cot x} - \frac{\sec x}{\csc x + \cot x} = 2\csc x$$

Objective 2: Use fundamental trigonometric identities to rewrite expressions.

[14.3.2.13] *Dynamic Item*

13. $\csc 2x + \cot 2x$ forms an identity with which of the following?

[A] $\cot x$  [B] $\tan \dfrac{x}{2}$  [C] $\cot \dfrac{x}{2}$  [D] $\tan x$

[14.3.2.14] *Dynamic Item*

14. Which of the following is equal to $\dfrac{2\sin^2 x + \cos 2x}{\csc x}$ ?

[A] $\dfrac{1 + \sin x}{\cos x}$  [B] $\dfrac{1 + \sec x}{\sec x}$  [C] $\sin x$  [D] $\dfrac{1 - \sin x}{\cos x}$

[14.3.2.15] *Dynamic Item*

15. Write the expression $\cot x(\cos x\tan x + \sin x)$ in terms of a single trigonometric function.

**Lesson 3:  Fundamental Trigonometric Identities**

[14.3.2.16]  *Dynamic Item*

16.  Write the expression csc $2x +$ cot $2x$ in terms of tan $x$ or cot $x$.

**Lesson 4:  Sum and Difference Identities**

Objective 1:  Evaluate expressions by using the sum and difference identities.

[14.4.1.17]  *Dynamic Item*

17.  Find the exact value of $\sin(-75° + 30°)$.     [A] 1     [B] $\dfrac{\sqrt{2}}{2}$     [C] $-\dfrac{\sqrt{2}}{2}$     [D] $-1$

[14.4.1.18]  *Dynamic Item*

18.  Find the exact value of $\cos(285°)$.

[A] $\dfrac{-\sqrt{6} + \sqrt{2}}{4}$          [B] $\dfrac{-\sqrt{2} + \sqrt{6}}{4}$          [C] $\dfrac{\sqrt{6} + \sqrt{2}}{4}$          [D] $\dfrac{-\sqrt{2} - \sqrt{6}}{4}$

[14.4.1.19]  *Dynamic Item*

19.  Find the exact value of $\cos(540° - 30°)$.

[14.4.1.20]  *Dynamic Item*

20.  Find the exact value of $\sin(345°)$.

Objective 2:  Use matrix multiplication with sum and difference identities to perform rotations.

[14.4.2.21]  *Dynamic Item*

21.  Find the image of $(1, -2)$ after a counterclockwise rotation of $90°$ about the origin.
$$\begin{bmatrix} \cos x & -\sin x \\ \sin x & \cos x \end{bmatrix}\begin{bmatrix} 1 \\ -2 \end{bmatrix}$$

   [A] $(-2, 1)$          [B] $(-1, -2)$          [C] $(2, 1)$          [D] $(1, -2)$

Algebra 2
311

**Lesson 4: Sum and Difference Identities**

[14.4.2.22] *Dynamic Item*

22. The coordinates of the vertices of a triangle are represented by the polygon matrix
$\begin{bmatrix} 0 & 1 & 6 \\ 0 & -1 & 9 \end{bmatrix}$. Which polygon matrix represents the image of the triangle under a 180°
counterclockwise rotation about the origin?

[A] $\begin{bmatrix} 0 & 1 & -1 \\ 0 & 6 & 9 \end{bmatrix}$  [B] $\begin{bmatrix} 0 & -1 & -6 \\ 0 & 1 & -9 \end{bmatrix}$  [C] $\begin{bmatrix} 0 & -1 & 1 \\ 0 & -6 & -9 \end{bmatrix}$  [D] $\begin{bmatrix} 0 & -1 & -6 \\ 0 & -9 & 1 \end{bmatrix}$

[14.4.2.23] *Dynamic Item*

23. Find the image of $(5, 3)$ after a counterclockwise rotation of 180° about the origin.

[14.4.2.24] *Dynamic Item*

24. The coordinates of the vertices of a triangle are represented by the polygon matrix
$\begin{bmatrix} -6 & 5 & -2 \\ -7 & -3 & 9 \end{bmatrix}$. Which polygon matrix represents the image of the triangle under a 180°
counterclockwise rotation about the origin?

**Lesson 5: Double-Angle and Half-Angle Identities**

Objective 1: Evaluate and simplify expressions by using double-angle and half-angle identities.

[14.5.1.25] *Dynamic Item*

25. Given $\sin \theta = -\dfrac{6}{13}$, where $\pi < \theta < \dfrac{3\pi}{2}$, find the exact values of $\sin 2\theta$ and $\cos 2\theta$.

[A] $-\dfrac{97}{169}, -\dfrac{12\sqrt{133}}{169}$    [B] $-\dfrac{12\sqrt{133}}{169}, \dfrac{97}{169}$

[C] $\dfrac{12\sqrt{133}}{169}, \dfrac{97}{169}$    [D] $-\dfrac{97}{169}, \dfrac{12\sqrt{133}}{169}$

**Lesson 5: Double-Angle and Half-Angle Identities**

[14.5.1.26] *Dynamic Item*

26. Find $\cos \frac{1}{2}A$ and $\sin \frac{1}{2}A$ if $\sin A = \frac{15}{17}$ and $A$ is a second-quadrant angle.

[A] $\cos \frac{1}{2}A = \frac{\sqrt{15}}{34}$, $\sin \frac{1}{2}A = \frac{2\sqrt{2}}{34}$    [B] $\cos \frac{1}{2}A = \frac{2\sqrt{2}}{34}$, $\sin \frac{1}{2}A = \frac{\sqrt{15}}{34}$

[C] $\cos \frac{1}{2}A = \frac{3\sqrt{34}}{34}$, $\sin \frac{1}{2}A = \frac{5\sqrt{34}}{34}$    [D] $\cos \frac{1}{2}A = \frac{5\sqrt{34}}{34}$, $\sin \frac{1}{2}A = \frac{3\sqrt{34}}{34}$

[14.5.1.27] *Dynamic Item*

27. Given $\sin \theta = -\frac{1}{9}$, where $\pi < \theta < \frac{3\pi}{2}$, find the exact values of $\sin 2\theta$ and $\cos 2\theta$. Leave the answer in rational or radical form.

[14.5.1.28] *Dynamic Item*

28. Find $\cos \frac{1}{2}A$ and $\sin \frac{1}{2}A$ if $\sin A = -\frac{3}{5}$ and $A$ is a third-quadrant angle.

**Lesson 6: Solving Trigonometric Equations**

Objective 1: Solve trigonometric equations algebraically and graphically.

[14.6.1.29] *Dynamic Item*

29. Solve $\cos x - \sqrt{3 - 3\cos^2 x} = 0$ given that $0° \leq x < 360°$.

[A] $30°, 330°$        [B] $30°, 210°$        [C] $30°, 150°$        [D] $60°, 300°$

[14.6.1.30] *Dynamic Item*

30. Find all solutions of $\tan x - \sqrt{1 - 2\tan^2 x} = 0$.

[A] $30° + n360°$, $150° + n360°$        [B] $60° + n360°$, $300° + n360°$

[C] $60° + n360°$, $120° + n360°$        [D] $30° + n360°$, $210° + n360°$

**Lesson 6: Solving Trigonometric Equations**

[14.6.1.31] *Dynamic Item*

31. Solve $\tan x - \sqrt{1 - 2\tan^2 x} = 0$ given that $0° \le x < 360°$.

[14.6.1.32] *Dynamic Item*

32. Find all solutions of $\sin x - \sqrt{3 - 3\sin^2 x} = 0$.

Objective 2: Solve real-world problems by using trigonometric equations.

[14.6.2.33] *Dynamic Item*

33. Jeremy starts the engine on his small private airplane. The engine drives a propeller with a radius of 7 feet and its centerline 10 feet above the ground. At idle, the propeller rotates at a constant speed of approximately 700 revolutions per minute. The height of one propeller tip as a function of time is given by $h = 10 + 7 \sin(700t)$, where $h$ is the height in feet and $t$ is the time in minutes. Find $h$ when $t = 5.5$ minutes.

[A] 3.4 ft          [B] 7.6 ft          [C] 16.6 ft          [D] 12.4 ft

[14.6.2.34] *Dynamic Item*

34. Suppose the depth of the tide in a certain harbor can be modeled by $y = 25 - 4\cos\left(\dfrac{\pi}{6}t\right)$, where $y$ is the water depth in feet and $t$ is the time in hours. Consider a day in which $t = 0$ represents 12:00 midnight. For that day, when are high tide and low tide and what is the depth of each?

[A] high tide at 6:00 a.m. and 6:00 p.m., depth 25 ft
    low tide at 12:00 noon and 12:00 midnight, depth 4 ft

[B] high tide at 12:00 noon and 12:00 midnight, depth 29 ft
    low tide at 6:00 a.m. and 6:00 p.m., depth 21 ft

[C] high tide at 12:00 noon, depth 25 ft
    low tide at 6:00 a.m., depth 4 ft

[D] high tide at 6:00 a.m. and 6:00 p.m., depth 29 ft
    low tide at 12:00 noon and 12:00 midnight, depth 21 ft

**Lesson 6: Solving Trigonometric Equations**

[14.6.2.35]  *Dynamic Item*

35.  Jacqueline is checking her bicycle's wheel. The wheel has a radius of 30 cm, and its center is 41 cm above the ground. Jacqueline is rotating the wheel at a constant speed of 160°/s. The height of a point on the tire as a function of time is given by $h = 41 + 30 \sin(160t)$, where $h$ is the height in centimeters and $t$ is the time in seconds. Find $h$ when $t = 10$ s. Round your answer to the nearest tenth of a centimeter.

[14.6.2.36]  *Dynamic Item*

36.  The motion of a ship riding at anchor can be modeled by $y = 20 - 5 \cos\left(\dfrac{\pi}{6}t\right)$, where $y$ is the water depth in feet and $t$ is the time in hours. Consider a day in which $t = 0$ represents 12:00 midnight. At what time during that day will the water under the ship be the deepest and what time will it be the shallowest, and what will the water's depth be at these times?

**Lesson 1: The Law of Sines**

Objective 1: Solve mathematical and real-world problems by using the law of sines.

[14.1.1.1] *Dynamic Item*

[1] [C]

[14.1.1.2] *Dynamic Item*

[2] [C]

[14.1.1.3] *Dynamic Item*

[3] $e = 33.9$, $G = 48°$, $E = 76°$

[14.1.1.4] *Dynamic Item*

[4] $A = 22.43°$, Area $= 88.75$ in.$^2$

**Lesson 2: The Law of Cosines**

Objective 1: Use the law of cosines to solve triangles.

[14.2.1.5] *Dynamic Item*

[5] [B]

[14.2.1.6] *Dynamic Item*

[6] [B]

[14.2.1.7] *Dynamic Item*

[7] $74.2°$

[14.2.1.8] *Dynamic Item*

[8] 27.2

**Lesson 3: Fundamental Trigonometric Identities**

Objective 1: Prove fundamental trigonometric identities.

[14.3.1.9]  *Dynamic Item*

[9]  [C]

[14.3.1.10]  *Dynamic Item*

[10]  [C]

[14.3.1.11]  *Dynamic Item*

$$\sin 3x = \sin(2x + x)$$
$$= \sin 2x \cos x + \cos 2x \sin x$$
$$= (2 \sin x \cos x)\cos x + (1 - 2 \sin^2 x)\sin x$$
$$= 2 \sin x \cos^2 x + \sin x - 2 \sin^3 x$$
$$= 2 \sin x(1 - 2 \sin^2 x) + \sin x$$
$$= 2 \sin x - 4 \sin^3 x + \sin x$$
[11]
$$= 3 \sin x - 4 \sin^3 x$$

[14.3.1.12]  *Dynamic Item*

$$\frac{\sec x}{\csc x - \cot x} - \frac{\sec x}{\csc x + \cot x} = \frac{\sec x\,(\csc x + \cot x)}{(\csc x - \cot x)(\csc x + \cot x)} - \frac{\sec x\,(\csc x - \cot x)}{(\csc x + \cot x)(\csc x - \cot x)}$$
$$= \frac{\sec x \csc x + \csc x}{\csc^2 x - \cot^2 x} - \frac{\sec x \csc x - \csc x}{\csc^2 x - \cot^2 x} = \frac{2 \csc x}{\csc^2 x - \cot^2 x} = 2 \csc x$$
[12]

Objective 2: Use fundamental trigonometric identities to rewrite expressions.

[14.3.2.13]  *Dynamic Item*

[13]  [A]

---

Algebra 2

[14.3.2.14]  *Dynamic Item*

[14]  [C]

[14.3.2.15]  *Dynamic Item*

[15]  $2\cos x$

[14.3.2.16]  *Dynamic Item*

[16]  $\cot x$

**Lesson 4:  Sum and Difference Identities**

Objective 1:  Evaluate expressions by using the sum and difference identities.

[14.4.1.17]  *Dynamic Item*

[17]  [C]

[14.4.1.18]  *Dynamic Item*

[18]  [B]

[14.4.1.19]  *Dynamic Item*

[19]  $-\dfrac{\sqrt{3}}{2}$

[14.4.1.20]  *Dynamic Item*

[20]  $\dfrac{-\sqrt{6}+\sqrt{2}}{4}$

Objective 2: Use matrix multiplication with sum and difference identities to perform rotations.

[14.4.2.21] *Dynamic Item*

[21] [C]

[14.4.2.22] *Dynamic Item*

[22] [B]

[14.4.2.23] *Dynamic Item*

[23] $(-5, -3)$

[14.4.2.24] *Dynamic Item*

[24] $\begin{bmatrix} 6 & -5 & 2 \\ 7 & 3 & -9 \end{bmatrix}$

**Lesson 5: Double-Angle and Half-Angle Identities**

Objective 1: Evaluate and simplify expressions by using double-angle and half-angle identities.

[14.5.1.25] *Dynamic Item*

[25] [C]

[14.5.1.26] *Dynamic Item*

[26] [C]

[14.5.1.27] *Dynamic Item*

[27] $\dfrac{8\sqrt{5}}{81}, \dfrac{79}{81}$

[14.5.1.28]  *Dynamic Item*

[28]  $\cos \dfrac{1}{2} A = -\dfrac{\sqrt{10}}{10}$, $\sin \dfrac{1}{2} A = \dfrac{3\sqrt{10}}{10}$

**Lesson 6:  Solving Trigonometric Equations**

Objective 1:  Solve trigonometric equations algebraically and graphically.

[14.6.1.29]  *Dynamic Item*

[29]  [A]

[14.6.1.30]  *Dynamic Item*

[30]  [D]

[14.6.1.31]  *Dynamic Item*

[31]  30°, 210°

[14.6.1.32]  *Dynamic Item*

[32]  $60° + n360°$,  $120° + n360°$

Objective 2:  Solve real-world problems by using trigonometric equations.

[14.6.2.33]  *Dynamic Item*

[33]  [A]

[14.6.2.34]  *Dynamic Item*

[34]  [D]

[14.6.2.35]  *Dynamic Item*

[35]  51.3 cm

[14.6.2.36]  *Dynamic Item*

[36]  high tide at 6:00 a.m. and 6:00 p.m., depth 25 ft
low tide at 12:00 noon and 12:00 midnight, depth 15 ft